Moonwalking

Moonwalking

Moonwalking

Rob Self-Pierson

Rob Self-Pierson
www.robselfpierson.com

Copyright © Rob Self-Pierson

Cover design by Karina Stolf
Typeset by Becca Souster
Editorial advice from Tim Rich

Printed and bound in Great Britain by Clays Ltd, Elcograf S.p.A.

A CIP catalogue record for this book is available from the British Library

ISBN 978-0-9933234-1-6

The characters and events in this book are as real as memory would allow. Some names have been changed.

For Mum and Dad

The Journey

Phase III—Waxing

Phase IV—Full

Sweet Moon, I thank thee for thy sunny beams;
I thank thee, Moon, for shining now so bright;
For by thy gracious, golden, glittering gleams,
I trust to take of truest Thisbe sight.

A Midsummer Night's Dream,
William Shakespeare

Prologue

In January 2009, four months after my first love left me without warning, I decided to go walking by the light of the full moon.

Those four months had dragged me into some very dark places. Without my girlfriend's hand in mine to keep me steady, I lost faith in everything, including myself. But, just before the turn of the year, a walk along a moonlit river and a tarot reading with a white witch offered me a sliver of hope.

The following twelve months were tough. So very tough. At times so tough and so lonely and so revealing of who I really was when by myself that sometimes giving up seemed the only option. Except I couldn't give up. Not when I realised what was starting to happen to me.

Before we go on, we should spend a little time with a very important character who appears often in this tale.

I'd like you to imagine for a moment you're in a room with one of those smart speaker devices. Feeling bored or lonely, you ask it to tell you a story about the moon. If it's connected to Wikipedia, it will say something like this:

The moon is an astronomical body that orbits planet Earth and is Earth's only permanent natural satellite. It is the fifth-largest natural satellite in the solar system, and the largest among planetary satellites relative to the size of the planet that it orbits (its primary).

The device will ask you if you'd like it to keep speaking. You'll imagine it's holding back the most colourful information, so you'll say 'yes'. It will go on to tell you:

The moon is thought to have formed about 4.51 billion years ago, not long after Earth. The most widely accepted explanation is that the moon formed from the debris left over after a giant impact between Earth and a Mars-sized body called Theia.

Next it will talk about the moon's synchronous rotation with the Earth, meaning it always shows the same side to our planet. It will tell you about the dark volcanic *maria* and impact craters. It will share that the moon is the 'second-brightest regularly visible celestial object in Earth's sky', after the sun.

The facts and figures will go on and on until eventually —long after you've left your house or fallen asleep—the device will reveal the romantic role of the moon in myth and lore, the Transylvania effect and biological tides theory, possibly even the story behind a gentle image like the old moon in the young moon's arms. Sadly you won't be there to hear about moon goddesses and lunar worship sites and moon days and monthly moonlit rituals in the era of Enlightenment.

I'm not sure the device will ever share with you that without the moon's gravitational influence, life on Earth would—some theories suggest—find it difficult to survive. Our planet could, over time, wobble wildly, causing extreme seasons and impossible living conditions. Here's Terje Wahl, deputy director general of the Department of Space and Earth Sciences at the Norwegian Space Centre, explaining:

'The relevant link between spin and orbit is very complicated, but in a simplified version you could think of it as being like an Olympic athlete in the hammer throw event. When a hammer thrower spins around before letting go, he could nearly be rotating on a pinpoint. But as soon as he releases the hammer, he takes a couple of awkward steps and flails his arms to keep from falling down.'

Your device could have told you that, right? It could have painted a picture of moonless Earth, the flabby giant, wobbling out of control, tumbling down if he's not careful, taking others with him. That might have made you late for your night out. That might have kept you from dozing.

If you've bought this book to read long lists of facts and figures about the Earth's moon, you've made a terrible mistake. If you're an astronomer looking for new discoveries, an astrophysicist looking for new data, or someone from NASA looking for a new recruit, I'm sorry. I think your spaceship has veered off course.

This book is two things. First, it's the story of thirteen moonlit walks around the British Isles, in which the author —ten years younger at the time; shy, nervous and naïve—meets and learns from moon goddesses, witches, astronomers and other moon lovers.

But it's also a tale of losing the love of your life and trying to find yourself again—in some weird, wild and wonderful places.

Introduction

A giant impact

I think we need to talk.

The six most dreaded words in the English language. Especially when they're served to you cold by a girl you imagined spending the rest of your life with.

As Belle perched on the corner of her parents' dining room table that sunny Sunday morning, and explained why she was leaving me, I wobbled like a moonless Earth.

'I love you,' she said. 'I love you but I'm not *in* love with you any more. It's over. I'm sorry.' The nineteen most dreaded words in the English language. Especially when Belle is your first love and you've been living together, three hundred miles from friends and family, in Falmouth, Cornwall, for the last year.

The picnics we'd put together with any spare cash we could find when we got our first jobs. The loving messages she'd leave throughout my notebooks, knowing they'd make me smile. The damp nights in our flat when she'd throw a blanket over us and somehow squeeze into my fleece with me. The countless mornings and evenings she'd sit on my lap, say I was a great guy and perfect boyfriend, and kiss me. As I realised that this morning meant no more tender memories, I began to sob.

In a desperate attempt to save us, I tried to reason with Belle, help her to see the mistake I felt sure she was making. But instead I blubbed exactly what she was expecting to hear. That things would change, that I'd grow up and become a real man, and that I hadn't meant to tease her so much for the habits I all of a sudden found adorable. I even told Belle I'd try to get into James Blunt, her favourite singer at the time.

'Stop, Rob, please,' she said, so calm and considered. 'Please, just stop. It's over. I've already moved on.'

August 30th 2008 shattered me into so many tiny pieces, I became almost impossible to put back together. Driving to my parents' house later that morning, I sang along to Belle's favourite James Blunt song. 'You're *beautiful*,' I wailed like a wild wolf. 'You're *beautiful*, it's true.'

My dad, on seeing tears streaming down my cheeks as I crawled into the house, could only sing, 'Dry your eyes, mate— there's plenty more fish in the sea'. In singing lyrics by the alt hip hop group The Streets, I realised my father had become cooler than me while I'd been away. This encouraged yet more salty tears to roll into an already stinging wound.

I hosed my parents with sadness that welled from somewhere so deep inside me I couldn't control it. Gasping for breath, I perched on the corner of Mum and Dad's dining room table.

'It's over,' I cried. 'She's already moved on.'

Over the next three months, I'd wake every morning at 3am to find Pain, Anger and Loss nibbling me like they were blood-hungry bed bugs. I asked my parents to buy me a sweet guitar, and taught myself miserable minor chords. I paired the chords with some clichéd poetry I'd written and performed it to myself late into the night. That only stopped because the neighbours threatened to call the council.

I was twenty-four years old and back at my parents' house, in the town of my childhood, feeling like a failure.

To make things worse, I couldn't get a job, and only found employment when my mum bashed on the door of a local marketing agency and told them her baby boy enjoyed writing. Like a good son, I went to work every morning and wrote words I didn't care about for people I never met. At lunchtime, I'd disappear to the bathroom, slump against the wall, scrunch my face up so tight it hurt, and weep until my eyes ran dry.

August became September became October became November. But the pain and the anger and the loss and later the fear that I'd never be happy again wouldn't leave me. They had become me.

'I just don't know how to move on,' I said to my mum, as we walked slowly along the towpaths of the River Lee one cold, dewy, moonlit evening.

'You will, Rob,' said Mum. 'Just give it time.'

'I've given it months, Mum,' I snapped, 'and I still miss her like it ended yesterday. Later, I'll play you a song I've—'

'She's looking beautiful tonight, Rob,' said Mum, stopping my offer mid-sentence and looking up.

'How can you be *so* insensitive? Yes, yes, I'm sure she is. She always looked beautiful. And I never told her enough, did I? You're right. *She* was right. Everyone's right except—'

Mum continued to look into space. 'Nanny Becky loved Phoebe. Do you like Phoebe?'

'What on earth are you talking about?'

'That's what Nanny Becky called the moon.'

'The same Nanny Becky who called clouds at night "night clouds" and rain in warm temperatures "heat spots"?'

Mum looked from the heavens to her moody son. 'I've had enough of you being like this, Rob. At some point you need to find a way to get on with your life. Let's just go home.'

The air, so bitterly cold, hung silent between us.

'I'm sorry, Mum,' I said, seeing the crispest, clearest, whitest, most precious-stone-like moon above. 'Why "Phoebe"?'

'You know what, Rob, I'm not sure. Your nan had a different name for everything. She'd call it a bomber's moon when she saw the light reflecting off a river like this. Never knew why.'

Mum pointed to the fine film on the water's surface. It rippled as a goose sprinted into flight, scattering little rays of silver in every direction.

'*Bomber's* moon? What an… adorable lady she must have been.'

'She was, Rob. She really was.'

Back home, I flicked through an encyclopaedia until I found a mention of Phoebe and the moon. It turned out Nanny Becky wasn't as odd as I'd thought. Phoebe, in Greek myth, was daughter of Ouranos, the sky, and Gaia, the earth, who together ruled the cosmos.

Ouranos was a complex character—both all-powerful and deeply insecure. To protect his position and because he thought them ugly, he imprisoned six of his children, but allowed the other twelve to roam free. Furious with Ouranos for what he'd done to some of their offspring, Gaia ordered her free sons and daughters to castrate their father. Which they did with glee. As Ouranos's testicles flew into the sea, he lost his powers. His second set of children— the Titans, including Phoebe—claimed these. According to legend, Phoebe got 'dominion over the Moon and its Essence'.

I told my parents this over a cup of tea the morning after my moonlit walk along the river. I felt strangely sympathetic for Ouranos—for both his insecurities and loss of testicles.

'Old Becky: not quite the mad bat we thought, eh?' joked Dad.

'Oi, show some respect,' Mum and I said in unison.

Damp, dark and full of fragrances. That's the memory I have of Debbie's cellar. Debbie herself was probably twenty years older than me, with skin like silk, and eyes like half-opened palace doors. They twinkled as she spoke.

'Have you had your tarot read before, Rob?' she asked.

'I haven't. No. Never really been into all this hocus-pocus mumbo-jumbo but I thought *what have I got to lose now?*' I paused. 'I mean… um… it sounds wonderful.'

Debbie smiled, put her gloved hand on mine and whispered through the haze of a scented candle: 'It's fine to be sceptical. Let's see if we can open your mind a little.'

Debbie's a white witch who runs a pagan store in Waltham Abbey, in a building that was once my parents' shoe shop. If you need to stock up on sage sticks or catch a dream, White Witch is the place to go. Mum had suggested I speak to Debbie about the moon, apparently a passion for Wiccans. I didn't know much about witches at the time but I secretly hoped this one could mend my broken heart. She'd offered to read my tarot.

As we started the reading, Debbie turned a card from the pattern she'd created. It was the Lovers.

'You've lost a love recently, Rob. The card won't tell me the details, but I can see from your eyes…'

'My *first* love. My Belle. Yes, Debbie. She left me. We were going to have roast dinner with her parents and grandma, which is usually very tasty, but before we'd even decided what sort of meat we were going to have, she told me she wasn't in love with me any more. Why did she say that, Debbie? What's wrong with me?'

'I'm sorry, Rob. The cards don't have every answer. All I can tell you is the Lovers card is now, where you are at this present moment. When we turn another card, we'll be able to see where your future might lead you.'

As Debbie was about to pull my second card, I had a flash-back to this same cellar fifteen years earlier, when the shop was Uptons. Dad would sort slippers in the darkness of this dungeon while I stood at the top of the stairs, quaking at the thought of the monsters that lurked beneath. I must have twitched.

'Are you ok, Rob?' asked Debbie.

I steadied myself.

'Yes. Of course. I'm fine, Debbie. Just thinking how spooky it was that you knew about me and Belle and our awful break-up.'

'The cards tell us, Rob. Not me. Let's see what you might have ahead of you.'

Debbie leant into the table and pulled a card decorated with sticks. She gently parted her frizzy black hair and whispered: 'A wand card suggests travel, Rob. Perhaps a journey, some time to explore. Does that mean anything to you?'

Later that evening, I told Mum and Dad what had happened in the cellar at White Witch.

'And she knew I'd lost my love. She knew about Belle. And her parents and grandma. And the roast dinner. And then, which is spookiest of all, she picked a *moon* card, Mum. And a wand card, which apparently is about travel. So I decided that the moon is probably quite important to me right now. That's why I think soon I might travel to an observatory to find out more about it. Her. Phoebe.'

'That's all rather exciting,' said Mum, slapping some mash on my dinner plate. 'Sounds like you might be about to have a little adventure. I'm very pleased to hear that. A new hobby.'

That night, like usual, I couldn't sleep. But for the first time in many months, it wasn't just thoughts of Belle keeping me awake. It was the idea of a date with a different lady, a lunar lady.

On New Year's Eve, I made a resolution. The first full moon of 2009, I'd visit the Royal Observatory in Greenwich to learn more about the distant rock that orbits us. I'd then walk to Waltham Abbey, back home to Mum and Dad, illuminated by the full moon. I'd share new knowledge with my parents, tell Debbie about my walk, and my heart would be mended. I could move on. It would be so simple.

Phase I

Waning

January

One small step

That's one small step for *a* man.

Apparently that's what Neil Armstrong was supposed to say when he left that first footprint on the lunar surface.

After all, 'That's one small step for *man*, one giant leap for *mankind*' doesn't make sense. It's a tautology, like saying: 'It's somewhere between thirteen and seventeen miles all the way from start to finish.'

Which is exactly the answer I'd just given my older brother at the entrance of the Greenwich foot tunnel, south of the River Thames in London, late one bone-bitingly bitter afternoon. He was padded like an Eskimo.

'But remember,' I continued: 'every great journey starts with one small step.'

'You're such a knob,' David replied, sitting on a wall beside the river. 'You said thirteen miles. I'm not walking seventeen.'

'It'll be fun,' I said, trying to convince us both. 'And it's somewhere *between* thirteen and seventeen.'

Nanny Becky's night clouds had arrived. After a sunny morning, the sky was now an eerie mix of murky mauves, half-lit by the sickly streetlights of the city.

'Thirteen miles of walking through London at night wasn't ever going to be fun,' said David. 'It was going to be exercise because somebody'—he looked to his left—'has become a fitness freak. And somebody *else* a lonely moon freak.'

Natalie, my brother's long-term girlfriend, was contorting her tiny frame like she was preparing for a night in a suitcase.

'Don't forget to do your stretches, boys,' she said. 'Seventeen miles is a *long* way. And cheer up, Dave.'

I turned to look at the Cutty Sark, the famous tea clipper, whose prow was pointing north across the river in the direction we were about to walk. David stood and half-heartedly stretched his calf. He then paced towards me.

'Somewhere between thirteen and seventeen miles, bro,' I said, hushed. 'I promise.'

On the top step of the foot tunnel, Natalie opened an A to Z of London.

'Let's move,' she said, following the spiral underneath the Thames. 'It's going to be totally dark soon. That's when full-moon baddies come out.' She made ghost noises and giggled.

'I don't know much about the moon,' I said to David, as Natalie disappeared underground, 'but it's probably easier to see it when it's dark. Because the moon's white and it stands out in darkness. Saying that, I think I once saw the moon in the day, when the sky was blue. I wonder if that's a blue moon.'

My brother patted me hard on my back. 'Wow. You really know your stuff, mate. Do tell me more.'

I'd spent the morning in the Royal Observatory. With almost no knowledge of space, I thought the great dome at the top of Greenwich Park would be the perfect place to bone up. In a morning, I'd master the moon. Then, in the afternoon, I'd wander back to Waltham Abbey. The full moon, which had so softly lit the River Lee in December, would shine on me, and heal me, so the next morning I'd wake happy and whole again, ready to let go of Belle and find a new love.

This was, looking back now, a naïve notion. The sort of narrative a lost soul likes to tell itself. But naïvety, I'd learn many times this year, can sometimes be a powerful propellant.

Back in London, that dark January afternoon, David, Natalie and I had crossed the river and reached a place called Three Mills.

'Did you know without the full moon Columbus might have been killed by the people of Jamaica?' I said, as we tried to navigate our way between warehouse buildings. 'Roger told me Columbus survived all thanks to an almanac.'

'Who's Roger?' asked David. 'And what's an almanac? And where the hell are we?'

'Roger is a scientist man I met in the Royal Observatory earlier. He told me about Christopher Columbus and James Cook and the Greenwich Meridian and all sorts of other cool moon stuff.'

'Scientist man?' asked Natalie. 'An astronomer?'

'*That's* the word.'

'Can't see how the moon can kill you, mate,' said David.

I rolled my eyes. 'It wasn't the moon that nearly killed him. It was the Jamaican people.

'Columbus and some of his crew had become castaways when shipworms devoured his fleet. At first, the natives welcomed the visitors. But after a few months, they got tired of feeding them for not much more than a few trinkets in payment. So they stopped making them food.'

'What about the moon?' asked Natalie.

'This is the genius part. The almanac gave Columbus information about the sun and the moon. From it, he could work out the next lunar eclipse...'

'Oh that's clever,' said Natalie. 'So he could pretend to predict it? Like he was some sort of god?'

'*Exactly*. Columbus threatened the local chief that if his men didn't get food then his Christian god would be furious and the full moon *inflamed with wrath*.'

'Pretty sure my knee's becoming inflamed with wrath,' said David, starting to limp.

'So that evening,' I continued, 'the moon appeared but, as Columbus predicted, something weird happened—instead of it looking like a normal white full moon, it looked red as it passed through Earth's shadow. Columbus's warning had come true.'

'So the natives,' summarised Natalie, 'thought Columbus was godly and began to feed his shipmates again. Brilliant.'

'Smart guy,' added David. 'What do you think he would've done if he'd got his brother lost in some warehouse complex?'

The sky continued to glow grimy orange as clouds like clumps of mud stopped us seeing the moon, which I assumed was somewhere above us. Natalie, still sprightly, was bouncing between buildings like a 90s computer game character, while David and I followed. We stepped onto a bridge.

'STOP NOW,' boomed a bodyless voice. 'STAND STILL. This is a secure zone. You are trespassing.'

David and I looked up, catching, for the briefest moment, the thinnest strip of full moon between clouds.

'Did you see that?' I asked him. 'Did the moon just...'

But the voice returned:

'Stand still. You must now approach the security office.'

'Do you want us to stand still or approach the security office?' David asked the voice.

29

'We cannot hear what you say,' said the voice. 'But we can see what you do.'

'Then what should we do?' I asked.

'Can't hear you,' replied the voice.

Natalie yanked David by the arm and we walked on. We soon came to a security hut and a small man in glasses standing as tall as he could behind the glass.

'This is private property. You cannot walk here.'

Natalie, stretching, responded, 'You should probably put some signs up saying that. And lock your gates.'

Thawing my face with my hands, I added, 'Why *is* it private around here? What happens at Three Mills?'

'That is top secret. I cannot tell you.'

'They film Big Brother,' said Natalie, passing around her phone.

'You need to leave now,' said the man.

Around seven miles into the walk, we reached Leyton. My mum had always forbidden me from hanging out here. Too dangerous, she'd said. Too much crime. Muggings, stabbings. Don't go out at night. Definitely not by full moon. And perhaps she'd been right to worry: even today, a look at the area's crime statistics isn't pleasant reading. Tonight, however, the streets were silent but for a shadowy man very politely asking us to push his broken-down Ford Escort out of the road.

Nanny Becky's night clouds were now dragging their dewy knuckles on the ground. The moon, Phoebe, I'd hoped our guardian angel and torch on the walk, still hadn't fully revealed herself. I started to worry that I'd misread my own almanac, which my mum had bought me for Christmas.

'You've gone quiet,' said David. 'What's wrong?'

What if I'd confused the dates? Or chosen the wrong moon phase? I'd read there were a few. What if not seeing the moon meant I wouldn't be healed? What if Walthamstow, the next town we'd reach, worse than Leyton according to my mum, was going to be the death of me?

The newspaper headline flashed before my eyes:

LONELY MOON FREAK MESSES UP WALK. GETS MURDERED.

'Come on, mate,' said David, patting me on the back. 'If we close our eyes, Walthamstow won't be *that* bad.'

But it felt worse than that. A panic, apparently sparked by the fear of messing up in front of my big brother and his girlfriend, had sent me spinning. The high street shops either side of me were laughing like demented clowns, their window displays giant, salivating mouths. The pavement had become sponge. Car lights were prisoner camp torches, hunting me.

I realise now that I was experiencing a form of anxiety. A feeling of dread, of doom, of guilt and unhappiness that outweighed the event that had led to it. This was negativity dredged up by another experience. And it was swamping me.

I continued to walk between David and Natalie, and share the moment with them in body, but my mind was in Falmouth, watching helplessly as Belle drifted out to sea. My breathing was quickening, shortening. My eyesight started to blur.

'What do you know about Walthamstow?' asked Natalie. 'Other than your mum telling you we'll all get murdered here.'

Her voice quivered around the outside of my ears.

Walthamstow. Murder. Mum. Pain. Anger. Loss. Belle. Oh Belle. Where are you, Belle? I need you now, Belle. Don't leave me, Belle. I love you, Belle. Nothing seemed real any more.

'Rob?' asked David, prodding me. 'You going to answer Nat?'

'Sorry, what?' I said, spiralling back into the cold night.

'I just wondered what you knew about this place.'

Trying to shake off my mad moment, I turned to Natalie and rubbed my eyes. 'Only that my old college friend James used to live here with his mum. But I haven't seen James in *years*.'

'James?' asked David. 'I remember Sam and Matt. Don't remember a James. Are you making up friends to impress Nat?'

And at that second, as my brother teased me again, James brushed past me, walking the opposite direction with a mate.

'Sorry,' he said. 'Oh. Y'all right, Rob?'

'Oh, hey mate,' I replied. 'You ok?'

'Yeah. Good to see you.'

And he was gone.

I turned to David. '*That* James,' I said, struggling to believe what had just happened. '*That* was James. We studied together. Then his girlfriend went to my uni. I haven't seen him in probably three years. Did that just happen?'

'I'll be honest with you, bro,' said David, watching James walk away. 'Didn't look like he's missed you that much.'

Phoebe hadn't shown her face. Not her whole face. A couple of times she'd winked from behind clouds. But if we'd been at sea, trying to locate ourselves using her position alongside the stars, which apparently had helped James Cook to circumnavigate the globe in the 18th century, we'd have been in big trouble.

In five hours, we'd walked about fifteen miles. I'd enjoyed being outside, seeing new places, bonding with David and Natalie, *doing* to stop thinking so much. But the whole point of tonight was to walk by moonlight and heal. I felt let down and sad. My brother had started to ask where the 'poxy moon' was. To begin with, I defended it. But secretly I was wondering the same.

As we passed two giant reservoirs not far from home, we turned to look at London, which was now a thin line of pulsing lights on the horizon. Then, just as I was pointing out to Natalie how icy and dangerous the puddles had become, David stepped on one. As his stocky frame thudded to the frozen ground, the moon finally smiled at me.

Natalie ran to David's aid, lifting his head from the pavement and checking both for cracks. I stood transfixed, looking up instead of down.

'The moon!' I said. 'The *full* moon. Look at her, Dave. Wow, Natalie. Gosh. Look. God. Wow. Dave, Nat, quick look.'

But they were too busy mopping my brother's bloodied head. By the time he was back on his feet, the clouds had returned. Neither David nor Natalie believed what I'd seen. And I'd have felt the same, looking at how leaden the sky appeared now. But I swear I saw the full moon at that moment. Had I not, the rest of my year could have been very different indeed.

The pub was warm, softly lit and rumbling with chatter.

Children were tearing around the decorative carpet, leaping onto their healthy knees and shouting stories to one another.

On a quiet table in the corner sat three weary night walkers and my parents. Mum was very impressed that we'd walked all that way: seventeen miles was the official distance.

'Blimey, what a long walk. And only one casualty.'

She put her hand on David's wet shoulder.

'Nearly died there, Ma. This moonwalking lark is danger-ous.' David turned to me. 'I'd stop now, mate, while you can still walk. Well, hobble.'

'What did you say?' I asked, sipping a pint.

'I was only joking, mate.'

I finished my beer. 'No, what did you call the thing we did this evening? What was the word you used?'

'Moonwalking. Like Michael Jackson.'

'I like it,' I said, standing in crippling pain that ran from my shoulders, down my spine and through my knees. 'Ready to finish our *moonwalk*, team?'

'What do you mean?' asked Natalie. 'We finished it.'

But we hadn't finished it—not the walk I'd planned. That needed to end at a mosaic in Waltham Abbey's church gardens. It was a mosaic I'd helped create at school. It pointed out where the Prime Meridian crosses my hometown. And it featured the sun and the moon, looking at each other.

'Oh come on,' I pleaded. 'I'd rather finish this together. I don't know if I have the willpower to do it alone.'

Neither David nor Natalie moved. I sat back down.

Then Mum very carefully reached into her handbag and pulled out a manila envelope. 'Rob, open it when you get to your mosaic. But please be careful with it. It's very special to me.'

Those final forty-five minutes along the busy country roads of Essex were agonising—in both the pain they caused my body and the deep sense of loneliness they revealed in me. As my family drove away, I tried to smile. But exhaustion had made a mess of me.

'Don't stop, Rob,' I said out loud. 'Don't stop. Not now. You've come so many miles. Just a few more steps.'

I walked on, with tears in my eyes and a determination to not give up, until I reached the frosted gardens. And there, kneeling beside the moon of the mosaic I'd helped conceive as a thirteen year old, I unstuck the envelope Mum had given me.

February

The bomber's moon

The crowd was made up mostly of tall, tubby, middle-aged men in woollies. I'd never seen so many beards, ponytails and cardigans in one place before. I was in the Kensington Conference Centre, west London, and it was time for Astrofest, the annual get-together of the brightest brains in the world of astronomy. And me.

'The gauge on this beauty stipulates at -0.34 degrees. When we're in retrograde, the third counter incredulates counter-clockwise at a velocity of twenty-four planetariums.'

That's possibly what the telescope salesman said as I walked past his stall. He was dwarfed by all but one of his machines. I nodded, smiled and asked him where the toilets were.

I'd come to Astrofest because of how much my brother had mocked my lack of moon knowledge during our January moonwalk. Once there, I experienced a revelation. One of those chance moments in life that sneaks up behind you, covers your eyes, spins you around, and gives you a big kiss on the lips.

In Kensington, among the big, bearded and brilliant, surrounded by science, overflowing with shyness and I'm sure looking horribly awkward, I picked up a leaflet that said: *2009—International Year of Astronomy.*

'Sorry, what's the International Year of Astronomy?' I asked the salesman.

'It's this year, young man. Of course you know it's four hundred years since Galileo first sketched the moon through a telescope? And forty years since the first moon landing?'

I counted back forty years. '1969?' I stated as a question. 'Really? Are you sure?'

'Of course I'm sure! You need to do some homework, my young friend. May I suggest you start by investing in the SkyBlaster 2000?'

As I joined the back of the winding queue to the toilets, which looked to snake a bladder-burstingly long way down the corridor, I read the reverse of the leaflet.

It set out the programme for the day. I could enjoy talks on sunspot cycles, the origin of the universe, and hear reports on constellation programs. Plus there was a presentation on Thomas Harriot, whose name I recognised from the news. Apparently this man was as important to moon studies as Galileo, who I'd definitely heard of before. During the day, I'd take in as much as my brain would allow. But first I really needed to wee.

'Excuse me,' I said to the woman in front of me. 'Is this queue for both men *and* women? I can't wait.'

'Sorry, what?'

'The queue. Men and women? Or is there a separate line for men? Just seems a bit long for the gents.'

The woman shook her head and tutted. 'I don't think Sir Patrick discriminates between men and women when he's signing books,' she said, turning away.

'Sir Patrick? Sir Patrick Moore? Here? Today? Signing books? The old bloke from Gamesmaster?'

The woman shook her head again, not bothering to look around this time. 'Why are you even here?'

'To do some homework,' I said to myself.

'Rob, you can't drive to Birmingham in this,' said Mum, pulling back the net curtains to reveal a sky as grey as concrete, and a family of cars sitting in half an inch of snow.

'I'll be fine, Mum, stop worrying. I need to moonwalk.'

'You *do* worry me though, Rob.'

I slipped outside and tried to open my car's frozen door.

'They're saying this is going to be one of the worst Februarys on record.' Mum was pacing on the doorstep before she stomped back inside.

I popped my head indoors. 'What would Nanny Becky have called weather like this?'

'No idea, Rob. But she would have called you mad for driving to Birmingham today.'

I managed to force open the passenger door and lean across to unfreeze the driver's side. 'Even if I was doing it to find out about the bomber's moon?'

As I sat in my car and put the key in the ignition, Mum stepped outside again and handed me the same manila envelope I'd opened by the mosaic. 'Just be careful. Please.'

From the envelope I slid out a black-and-white photograph and carefully blew away a speck of dirt.

'It's such a great photo, Mum,' I said, looking at Nanny Becky and my grandad George sitting together on the curve of a model of a crescent moon. They looked a little embarrassed but happily in love. 'Why haven't you shown me it before?'

'You never paid any attention to Phoebe before,' said Mum, taking back her photo. 'Rob. Be careful please. For all of us.'

Backpack? Check. Satnav? Check. List of things to see? Check. Moon books to read, including a very recently signed copy of Sir Patrick Moore's *On The Moon*? Check. I was ready to go moonwalking. Handbrake off. Ignition on. Battery dead. Sigh. Slide down hill. Hill start. Tired chug. And I was off. As I skated from side to side along the street, I could just about hear

Mum shout, for the final time, 'Be careful!'

The Moseley Arms was a recently renovated locals pub in an area of Birmingham called Digbeth. I remember thinking at the time that it seemed a long way from the canals of the city centre that I'd need for my walk.

A short lady with a strong Midlands accent showed me to my room.

'Here long?' she asked, like she hoped the answer was 'no'.

'Just two nights. For the full moon.'

'Good. Would you like dinner?'

'Yes please. I'm very hungry.'

'We don't do dinner on a Sunday,' she told me. 'But I can point you in the direction of somewhere that does.' And with that offer, she closed the door and left.

I went without food that night. Instead, I sat in my room and used my finger to trace the canals of Birmingham on a map, while I read stories of the Luftwaffe and started to understand what Nanny Becky had meant by a bomber's moon. Any time I caught myself skipping a sentence and thinking about Belle, I stopped and refocused. It worked the first few times. But as the bed grew bigger and colder, I decided to sleep through the loneliness. Well, I tried.

I wrapped a pillow around my head to block out the world, but I could hear the band downstairs. 'Don't Stop'. 'I Saw Her

Standing There'. 'Let's Stick Together'. And, just as I was drifting off, this from Creedence Clearwater Revival:

> *I hear hurricanes a-blowing*
> *I know the end is coming soon*
> *I fear rivers overflowing*
> *I hear the voice of rage and ruin*

> *Don't go 'round tonight*
> *Well, it's bound to take your life*
> *There's a bad moon on the rise*

I worried I was being sent a warning.

It was a month since my London walk with David and Natalie, my fellow moonwalkers. My knees felt healthy again but my nights remained long and lonely. Though they were often preferable to days, where I'd lose hours thinking about all the things Belle and I hadn't achieved together.

I'd started to receive, and to mostly ignore, techniques from friends for dealing with my feelings. Some said to jump into bed with the next girl I met. Others said to list all the stuff I hated about Belle: bad habits, mean comments she'd made. That quickly became a list of what I missed about her, a sort of mushy eulogy. One person even suggested I track her down and tell her how much I still loved her and that I'd do anything she wanted to be back with her. I tried each of these on paper, but none felt right. Instead, I continued to be hollow, like somebody had opened my chest and let my heart drift away on a breeze.

The next morning in Birmingham, I slipped miles across slushy puddles and sloshed through dirty snow towards the city centre canals. With the streets empty, I continued to the Pen Museum, which had sounded so dull I hoped it would feed my negative energy. There were no other visitors inside. The guide, an intense man with bramble-bush hair on just the sides of his head, approached as soon I walked in. Within a minute, he'd handed me a fountain pen.

'It's nice,' I said to Arthur, whose bristly eyebrows were tangled like junction box wires. 'I haven't held one of these since school. It's definitely nicer than modern ballpoints—'

As I was about to take a silver biro from my backpack, Arthur put his hand on mine and stopped me. 'We don't mention the b-word in here,' he said, handing me a collection of nibs. 'Do you like nibs?'

I picked one up. 'I like *this* nib.'

'That's a semilunar,' said Arthur. 'You see its shape?'

'"Lunar" as in moon?'

'Precisely. It's a crescent moon shape.'

I held it between my fingers, studying it like it was a rare gem, while Arthur knelt down to dig out an illustration from a drawer. I held the nib up to the image, which looked more like a medieval spear than slice of moon to me. I didn't mention that to Arthur though, who was admiring his nib collection and illustrations like they were his babies.

A caption below the illustration read:

Figs 2 are back and side views of the flat spade; or as some of the Birmingham makers style it, the Lunar pen.

Arthur twizzled his wiry white hair around his finger and continued our tour of the museum. He showed me the Pen Room, designed to recreate the feel of a traditional pen factory. He pointed out and named various pens in different cases, and shared who'd created each. As his passion flowed like ink, I imagined Arthur was the happiest man alive. I felt a little jealous.

'At its height, the pen trade in Birmingham employed 8,000 people, over 70% of whom were women,' said Arthur. 'During the mid-19th century, if you used a pen, it had probably been made in Birmingham, in one of the many factories you'll find lining our streets and canals.'

At the end of the tour, Arthur handed me back the semilunar nib he'd been caressing as we walked. He then shook my hand and wished me luck with my journey. I told him I hoped the nib would bring me the luck, and keep the clouds away.

'The beauty of the moon is that it's always there,' said Arthur, 'regardless of the weather.'

The weather that February afternoon was hard. Five below and dropping fast. Clouds had patched the sky again, like in London last month, and what I thought was the moon turned out to be a distant sun trying its best to burn through. This time I knew it was the full moon phase though—not new, first quarter, third quarter, crescent or gibbous, words I'd recently learned.

With the blood in my fingertips beginning to freeze, I ducked into a pub for a pint of beer and some chips. While Elvis sang a slow 'Blue Moon' to me through the speakers, I used my semilunar nib and a blob of leftover ketchup to write the words 'alone', 'dream' and 'love' onto a serviette.

Looking outside, I faced up to the fact I wasn't going to see Phoebe tonight. But as I'd invented the concept of moonwalking, and because of Arthur's wisdom, I decided it was ok. It was also ok to walk the night before or after a fully full moon because Debbie had told me the full moon is powerful for those three days. Starting my second pint, I used my biro to scribble a few rules for a moonwalk. Two hours passed before I realised I should probably be outside.

Back on the streets, my beer jacket wrapped tight, I ploughed on. Ploughed being the word, as snow was falling thick. It brought a moon-like glow to the empty streets.

Police had cordoned off the canals of the Soho Loop, making the factory tour I'd created on my map forbidden.

Curious to know just how dangerous a winter's walk beside a canal in a snowstorm might be, I stepped around the police tape and walked about two miles before I got my answer; I could no longer see my hands in front of my face. I panicked.

The air was dense with snow, and the slushy puddles from earlier had iced over. I wrapped my scarf higher around my face and head, thinking back to my brother's fall. At least he'd had Natalie there to pick him up. There were no other moonwalkers out tonight.

With each slip and slide back to the restaurants of Brindley Place, I sobered up a little more.

The Real Food Company. Pizza Express. Café Rouge. Adult World. The city centre had changed a lot since Nazi planes used the full moon's reflection in canals to guide them through Birmingham, where they unloaded 2,000 tonnes of bombs that killed 2,241 people.

Parts of Britain's second largest city—targeted for its Spitfire and Lancaster factories, rifle factories, factories making army vehicles and other equipment crucial to the war effort—were left in ruins.

I approached a war memorial depicting six wounded soldiers beside the cross. Weeping women and their babies looked on. Wiping away wet snow, I read the inscription:

Of 150,000 who answered the call to arms
12,320 fell: 35,000 came home disabled
At the going down of the sun in the morning
we will remember them
See to it that they shall not have
suffered in vain

I've since travelled through the battlefields of northern France and Belgium and paid my respects to those who were killed there. But the numbers, almost always in their thousands, are still staggering. And to think that Phoebe, so pretty and so peaceful, was used to aid such a waste of life. That her soft light, flickering on the water's surface, had led to such destruction, by both the Nazis and the Allies.

Tonight, with the bomber's moon now retired, all that fell from the sky was yet more snow. As I fixed my focus on the middle distance, it floated peacefully to the street, leaving a clean and satisfying crunch underfoot. Lit by streetlamp rather than moonlight, the snow created a path that led me to the Moseley Arms, where I stayed downstairs for a pint and a read.

'You missed the band last night,' said the lady who never did tell me where to go for dinner. 'Nothing like that in here tonight. But you're better off inside than out in that wild winter weather. Only stupid people go out in this.'

I was reading Jenny Uglow's *The Lunar Men*, about a group of industrialists, natural philosophers and intellectuals—including Erasmus Darwin, grandfather of Charles; mechanical engineer, James Watt; and potter, Josiah Wedgwood—who, in the 18th century, would meet across Birmingham by full moon. Phoebe gave them more light to navigate the city than the occasional gas lamp, and a regular date to put in the diary. They liked to call themselves 'Lunaticks'. I'd say they were early moonwalkers.

My watch clicked around to 11pm and the Moseley Arms closed its doors for the night. Looking out of my cold room, I watched as night clouds released snowflakes onto the city. I felt less negative than the night before. Perhaps it was Arthur's passion for semilunar pen nibs. Or my new knowledge of the Lunar Society, my kindred spirits. Or my memory of Sir Patrick Moore telling me my moonwalking was important. Maybe it was just watching nature reclaim the city outside, and being grateful I lived in a relatively peaceful period of history.

Whatever it was, after a couple of months of getting out and meeting people, moonwalking was starting to taste a little moreish. The difference in my emotions between two consecutive evenings made me wonder whether there might actually be something in this moon thing.

But a night with an old friend one month later would thud me back to a place I'd never, ever wanted to visit again.

March

And then he said it

'Touch it,' said Mark, holding open his flowery shirt. He pushed his chest towards me. 'Touch it and tell me what you think. Go on. You're going to be impressed.'

I took as large a step backwards as I could in the spare room of his mum's house. 'I think I'd rather not to be honest, Mark,' I said. 'Maybe after dinner.'

He stepped in, grabbed my hand and placed it on his naked pec. 'Impressive, right? I've only been back there a week. Did I tell you what happened when the girl—beautiful girl, mate, stunning girl, her eyes were all over me—when she signed me up? I fucking love the gym.'

Mark was a friend from my life with Belle in Falmouth. He'd got to know me as well as anyone did that year in the South West, except for Belle. Mark—his hair always slicked back, his flowery shirts always ironed and half-unbuttoned, his chest as skeletal as mine, and his mind constantly whirring with stories—had become a confidant while I was away from old friends. He was the person I'd go to when I needed perspective. He was also one of the first people I'd spoken to after Belle dumped me.

Slowly doing his shirt back up, Mark asked what the plans were for our time together.

'You mentioned something about getting in a fight,' he said, his eyes grinning. 'Did I tell you what happened when my brother and I fought twenty gypsies outside a pub? Think that was on a full moon. I love the full moon. Got loads of stories for you.'

'Great,' I said to Mark, pulling a jumper from my suitcase. 'Well, violence is what we're after. So it sounds like you're a perfect companion.' I laughed nervously.

'Amazing. But why me really? And why Brighton?'

'I've read that East Sussex Police did a study into violence around the time of full moon. Something about more fights and more accidents. And definitely something about more money going into putting police on the streets. Plus you're a mate and I wanted to hang out with you.'

Mark leant in and gave me a very long hug. 'Mate, you're a sweetheart. And I know about the study. Give me a minute and I'll see what I can do for us.'

Within half an hour, Mark had arranged for us to meet a policewoman called Alice, and two firemen called Trev and

Davo. We'd see them the next evening in Brighton.

'Really? That's brilliant. You're good at this.'

'No problem, mate,' said Mark, flexing his muscles. 'We've become close over the years, me and the police.'

What a difference a month makes. Tonight, I was in Battle, a short drive inland from England's south coast. As Mark and I strolled the silent streets of the little town, famous as the place Norman invaders defeated King Harold and his army in 1066, Phoebe gave us her full attention.

It was midnight, and we were bathing in the light of a perfect full moon. We had bottled beers and bags of crisps in our back-packs, and the town to ourselves. I must have stopped us twenty times to just pause, look up, breathe, smile and wonder. To sip from a sky so smoothed by moonlight that I could imagine jumping into it, snuggling up and drifting off into a lifetime of happy baby sleep. And then he said it.

'You know Belle put her Facebook status to "single" about six months before you two broke up?'

Mark swept an out-of-place hair back into position.

'I didn't. But when we split up, she did say she'd made her decision six months earlier. So it makes sense. Even though apparently she told my friend Matt she could imagine marrying me. That was only a few months before she ended it.'

'Seen her new guy?'

'Mark, please,' I said, slow and focused. 'Stop.'

The moonshadow cast by my frame froze in front of me. Immediately a second shadow appeared, shorter than mine, hair shoulder-length, body curving. The two shapes danced happily together, like flames in a hearth. They circled and spiralled and entwined their limbs. Until a third shadow appeared and snatched the second away.

'Sorry, they might not be together'—Mark paused—'just they looked *verrrry* close in that photo I saw last night.'

Within a second I'd been shot back to September the year before. Two weeks after the split. To the night my parents had gone on holiday to somewhere romantic. The first night I'd been alone since the break-up. I was there, like Scrooge with the Ghost of Christmas Past, watching Younger Rob log in to Belle's email account to find answers, but begging him not to.

Ten seconds later I was there, heavy on Younger Rob's shoulders, as he opened the email from Phil, Belle's Falmouth colleague he'd heard so much about and encouraged Belle to befriend. 'Yes of course go for lunch with him. He sounds nice.'

I was there when Younger Rob read the 'missing you so much' and the 'love you' and the 'kiss kiss kiss'. There when he opened the attachment and cracked in front of the photo of them embracing. I was there, watching Younger Rob self-destruct: cry, punch, bite, scratch, tear at himself.

Walking to the fence that overlooks Battle's battlefield, squeezing a beer bottle as tight as I could, drowning now in murderous moonlight, in the spotlight, my ego was pulling up life from six months earlier. The phone conversation with Belle's faux-friendly mum. The desperate attempts to get answers from her, then pleading to be passed to her daughter. The breathing too hard, too shallow, too fast. The joining Facebook, seeing a very happy-looking Belle doing all the things we used to enjoy together, and deleting my account immediately.

And a second later I was there in the passenger seat beside Younger Rob as he took his car out following far too many wines and took far too many corners far too fast because he had no idea how to stop the hurt. It had become a furious wasp determined to keep stinging.

'You ok, mate?' asked Mark, popping the top off another bottle and climbing over the gate onto the dewy grass.

The next two hours were consumed by heart-opening and reminiscing. I spoke as much to Phoebe as I did to Mark. Some smiles emerged when I told stories of happier times together. But mostly I was picking at a still-raw wound, and hoping to find a plaster that wouldn't fall off.

In the lead-up to the March full moon, a New Yorker called Louis had contacted me on Twitter. He told me the moonwalks

I'd mentioned were exciting to him, and more significant than I realised. He thanked me for building a relationship with the moon, and congratulated me for my efforts. His distant kindness had humbled me. Louis also introduced me to a book called *The Lunar Effect*, which featured moon theories developed by its author, the retired professor Arnold Lieber.

In the 1978 edition of his book, Lieber—'one of the most prominent authorities on the emerging science of cosmobiology', so it says, uncredited, on the back cover—argues for the ways the moon affects who we are and how we live, from our mood, to our mental health, to our sex drive.

'The scope of the investigation,' he writes, 'ranges from the observation of laboratory animals to the collection of worldwide weather data. The odyssey takes us from the depths of outer space to the still-being-explored workings of human biological systems.'

I paraphrased this for Mark the next evening as I drove us an hour through countryside from Battle to Brighton, where Alice, Trev and Davo were waiting for us.

'There's *definitely* a connection, I reckon,' said Mark, as we climbed a steep hill in my tired old car. 'I get fucking horny by full moon, mate. Did I ever tell you the time I—'

'YES!' I shouted across to Mark, who was shocked into silence. 'You did. When you were a chef? Or a rock star? Or an actor who was actually a barman? Yes. You've told me. Lots. Many times. You've told me everything about you today, mate.'

And with that outburst, that very second, we drove into fog. The clear sky, the moonlight that had been illuminating the gentle hills, like it did the field in Battle the night before, had vanished. We'd been choked, and visibility was down to less than a metre. Impossible to drive, I pulled over. After a minute of nothing but breathing, I turned to Mark and said sorry.

'It's ok,' he said. 'Did I ever tell you the story of when I was a counsellor and helped a woman who couldn't say sorry?'

With the smile back on his face, the fog rolled away over the hills, the sky relaxed and the moon returned.

An hour later, we were drinking herbal tea with Alice from East Sussex Police. She had a warm, open face and laughed far more than I'd expected a policewoman to laugh.

'So how did the investment work?' I asked, curious to know how moon money is spent in the emergency services.

'Andy, Inspector Andy Parr, commissioned some research into the relationship between violence and the full moon. He'd always wondered about it. But we wanted facts so we could get more police on the streets that time of month.'

'What did he find?'

'Results suggested there was a direct correlation between full moon and disturbances. Everyone seems to dismiss it as an old wives' tale. But we're sure there's something going on.'

I told Alice about Arnold Lieber and the apparent rise in testosterone levels and the charging of emotions at full moon.

'We've spoken to ambulance staff, too,' said Alice. 'They say they're called out far more at full moon. Coincidence?'

'The lunar effect,' I said, turning to Mark, feeling a little smug.

'If the moon's gravitational pull can control the tides of the Earth,' he replied, 'which is made up of around 71% water, and we're made up of around the same percentage, surely it must affect us too. Our moods, our emotions, our behaviour.'

'How on earth do you know that much detail about the biological tides theory?'

Mark grinned. 'I told you I used to be a professor, right?'

We waved goodbye to Alice and left the café.

'Well that was *illuminating*,' said Mark. 'Time to see the team at the fire station and start the next *phase* of our research.'

It was a Wednesday evening and groups of friends were gathering for drinks in Brighton's winding lanes and seafront bars. The air was blowing cool off the water, though I was ready for spring, which I could sense was gambolling in the next field. The town felt well behaved and peaceful. Either Andy Parr's extra investment was scaring criminals from the streets, or violence was a little more complicated than East Sussex Police liked to believe.

Inside Brighton's fire station, Davo—who was the size of a small planet—offered me and Mark a butterfly cake. Some had pink icing, the others yellow.

'We make them sometimes,' said Trev, a narrower man but just as solid. 'I'll go get you a cuppa.'

While Trev and Davo were telling me about the extra incidents they had to deal with each full moon, my mind drifted to a happy memory of eating ice cream with Belle at the top of a row of cute cottages in Cornwall. This sort of daydreaming kept happening. The street was called Stippy Stappy, which we both found adorable. My parents were visiting for the week, and Mum was trying to take a photo of Belle below the street sign. My girlfriend got ice cream on her nose, which of course I kissed away. Kissing your partner's nose is the sort of ritual that emerges in a long relationship. It's one of those soppy couple things you realise you miss so much when it's taken from you.

'I'm not sure about the whole moon effect thing to be honest,' shouted Trev, emerging later from the toilets. 'Seems unlikely to me. It's just a rock.'

'Nonsense,' said another voice from the kitchen. 'Must be true. Think about tides. They're water, we're water.'

'How does everyone know the tides theory?' I asked.

A woman who'd been reading the paper emerged from her article. 'The sea's huge. We're tiny. There's a big difference.'

'I agree,' said a young woman, buffing a badge. 'Though I'd really like to believe it influences us. I mean think of all the songs and stories and art and everything. There's magic in the moon.'

There's magic in the moon. Just three months into the year and I was starting to believe that a little. Three months of moonwalking and I'd already uncovered Columbus and the eclipse, Nanny Becky's bomber's moon, her photo with my grandfather, semilunar pen nibs, and I was now debating the moon's effect on humans with the fire brigade. I thanked the team as we headed back outside.

Mark had a determined look in his eyes now. On every street corner, he shared something unsavoury with a stranger. In front of a busy bar by the seafront, he shoulder-barged a giant of a man, then braced himself for a punch. But nothing. The sky was clear, the moon bright, and the atmosphere in town very relaxed.

We ended up doing a little pub crawl, with Mark on pints and me on lime and soda. Inside a pub near the seafront, Mark tried to summarise our moonwalk.

'So, we haven't been in any fights, which is a shame. Sorry about that. But we've learned the moon definitely has an effect on our behaviour because of what all my mates told you. Or it doesn't. Because nobody agrees.'

'So that's pretty conclusive then. Hey, at least I think we can agree there's magic in the moon.'

'And a little guy called Endymion,' said Mark. 'The man in the moon. From the John Lyly play. Written in the late 16th century, I think. Or early 17th. I should know that.'

I shook my head. 'You weren't an Elizabethan playwright as well, were you?'

Mark smiled. 'Hey, sorry about last night, mate, and the

whole Belle thing. I didn't realise it was so raw still. Probably shouldn't have mentioned her new love—'

'Mark! Stop!' I said, like I was talking to a dog.

'Sorry, Rob. Look, I think there's one thing we can *definitely* agree on,' said Mark, standing and unbuttoning his shirt. 'My chest is *way* more impressive than yours.'

He stumbled towards the toilet, turning by the door to shout: 'Don't get in any fights while I'm gone, my moon friend. That wouldn't be fair.'

That's when the very tall, smelly man with the long shorts and the torn t-shirt sat next to me and put his hand on my thigh.

'Mark!' I shouted to my friend. 'Mark!'

But Mark had gone.

Phase II

New

April

Searching for something

My car had died. After tens of thousands of miles together, mostly taking me and Belle between our parents' homes and Falmouth, she'd given up on me too. With her passing, I feared that a collection of memories would now fade.

I, thankfully, hadn't even been punched in Brighton. But I feel I'd got close. The very tall, smelly man with the dreadlocks and wicked grin who'd sat next to me in the pub was one of the strangest people I've ever met.

'You know the kelpies?' he'd asked, squeezing my knee as I tried to gulp down my lime and soda.

'I don't,' I replied, to be polite.

'You don't *want* to know the kelpies.'

I remember the gap created by his missing tooth, and how it made me think of a trap door.

'They'll take you,' he went on, acting out his words. 'They'll take you to their pool deep in the forest. You'll be mesmerised by the swirling and the curling and the whirling of the water. They come out when the moon is full, you see. They like the full moon. I think *you* like the full moon.'

His arms danced like he was in a rave.

'They'll be sirens to you, the treacherous water creatures, changing from equine apparition to beautiful young woman, singing under the light of the full moon. But then'—he threw his arms out like they'd been stifling an explosion—'they'll drag you down. And down. And further down into the depths...'

The man, now laying on the pub carpet, looked up, cackled and began to recite a poem in a strong Highlands accent:

> '...*When thowes dissolve the snawy hoord*
> *An' float the jinglin' icy boord*
> *Then, water-kelpies haunt the foord*
> *By your direction*
> *And 'nighted trav'llers are allur'd*
> *To their destruction...*'

To my surprise, nobody else in the pub was paying any attention to the crazed creature performing Robert Burns from the carpet. Even when he screamed:

'Beware the kelpies, my dear moon friend! Beware.'

With that warning, he stood and walked away.

I turned to Sam, whose idea it had been for us to drive to Whitby for an April moonwalk. 'Beware the kelpies!' I screamed, in my best Highlands accent. 'That's what the man told me last month. I reckon we should listen to him. They sound scary to me.'

I was rocketing along in my dad's car, which had a lot more power than my Fiesta. We passed a sign for Northampton.

'Kelpies sound cool,' said Sam. 'I hope we find some in Whitby.'

'I sort of hope we find some peace and quiet.'

Sam was an old school friend, and a young man who liked being scared. As a teenager, he'd often invite me to his house to play computer games and watch horror films. I'd always make an excuse to leave just before the movie started. My dislike of the genre probably dates back many years to an evening my parents were away and my brother forced me to watch Stephen King's 'It' by tying the living room doors closed. As soon as Sam heard about my moonwalks, he made the connection between horror, the full moon and *Dracula*—and he booked us a trip to Whitby, the Yorkshire town that had inspired the story.

I knew *Dracula*—I'd read the novel at university—and I liked Sam's enthusiasm. But I wasn't as keen as him. Killer clowns and shoe shop cellar monsters last long in the memory.

Sam grinned across to me from the passenger seat. 'As I said, you'll have *loads* of fun. And I'll be there to look after you.'

A few hours later, we parked close to our hotel.

'Before I forget,' I said. 'My dad's asked if we'd do something for him. He wants us to take a photo.'

'Of what? Something scary?'

'A statue of someone called William Scoresby. Apparently he's a relative of a man who knew my grandad. Dad said Scoresby invented the crow's nest, so there's a statue dedicated to him. Because of the family connection, Dad wants a photo.'

'Cool, we can do that,' said Sam. 'First, let's find Dracula.'

Whitby is a fishing village in the north east of England. Tomorrow we'd hang out here before walking down the Yorkshire coast to Robin Hood's Bay, taking in thirteen churches along our route. After a lot of soul searching recently, I wondered if religion might offer me the healing I needed. But tonight we had a vampire to get to know.

Beside a fish and chip shop, we found a short man in a top hat. He was waiting for us.

'My final two victims,' he cackled, turning on his heel. 'Excellent. Follow me.'

In preparation for the trip, I'd reread Bram Stoker's novel, looking for the moon. Research had also led me to skim Robert Stevenson's *Jekyll and Hyde*, Mary Shelley's *Frankenstein* and other horror literature I'd been made to read at university. The moon references were countless: from 'the moonlight struggling through' Shelley's closed shutters, conjuring images of the monster who would make her name, to the moonlit night that Mr Hyde murders Sir Danvers Carew.

In *Dracula* I found this scene, where Mina Murray heads out late at night into Whitby to track down her best friend, Lucy, who she finds too late to save from the vampire:

> *There was a bright full moon, with heavy black, driving clouds, which threw the whole scene into a fleeting diorama of light and shade as they sailed across. For a moment or two I could see nothing, as the shadow of a cloud obscured St. Mary's Church and all around it. Then as the cloud passed I could see the ruins of the abbey coming into view, and as the edge of a narrow band of light as sharp as a sword-cut moved along, the church and churchyard became gradually visible.*

That night could have been tonight, with the heavy black, driving clouds playing peekaboo with the full moon. Throughout our tour of the town, Sam stayed on the shoulder of our guide, Harry, as he walked us from landmark to landmark, pointing out where Mina, Lucy and other characters conduct their chilling game of cat and mouse with the monster.

Harry was a short man with wind-whipped eyebrows and

an impish smile. Any time he wanted to demonstrate how Dracula had attacked a victim, he grabbed Sam by his shoulder and punched his canines into my friend's neck.

'If you look up,' said Harry, 'you'll see a hotel. No ordinary hotel. From the Royal Hotel, Mr Abraham "Bram" Stoker wrote a lot of the novel that brings us here tonight.

'Stoker would wander the town of Whitby, much like we have this evening, speaking to the locals and listening to their stories by the light of the moon. The shipwrecks, the ghostly apparitions: they all made their way into his greatest work.'

As we looked up to the façade of the Victorian hotel, and a window that was reflecting milky moonlight, the dog of a man on the tour began to yap. Its owner apologised: 'He doesn't normally do this.'

Harry smiled: 'The spirit of the vampire is within the hound.'

Later, Harry silenced our chatter and looked us each in the eye, one by one, including the dog, as he gave a final speech:

'I'll leave you with this: tonight, alone in your beds, while the dogs bark and the full moon lights the ruins of the abbey and you wake with a sharp pain in your neck, remember it's too early for mosquitoes. Good night and sweet dreams.'

With that, he launched one final attack at Sam, who squealed in pleasure. The dog began to howl.

After a pub dinner, Sam asked if we'd done our moonwalk. 'Harry was great,' he said, 'but not very scary. And it's only nine o' clock and we've driven like a hundred hours and we haven't seen any kelpies yet.'

He pointed to some steps that led to a church.

'Do you remember the story Harry shared about Dracula as a black dog, jumping from the ship to the graveyard and disappearing into the night?'

Sam's eyes glowed like two full moons.

'Definitely not. No. I'm not doing it.'

We turned and looked up to St Mary's, a tiny church dwarfed by the remains of the abbey.

'We definitely should,' said Sam. 'Come on. It's a moonwalk.'

He started to climb the 199 steps. I followed. Slowly.

But within ten minutes, we were larking around in the graveyard like a couple of naughty school kids, howling at the moon and telling each other our best ghost stories. I told Sam the tale about the cellar, the white witch and the hideous monsters I imagined lurking there.

'See,' said Sam, 'there's no need to be scared.'

I held out my camera and half-pressed the shutter. 'Show us your fangs,' I said, not bothering to line up the shot. *FLASH*.

Back in the pub, with Dracula nowhere to be seen, but feeling quite brave after hanging out in the graveyard, I answered some of Sam's moon questions.

'How far is the moon from Earth?'

I explained to Sam how the moon orbits Earth in an

elliptical shape, which means sometimes it's as close as 225,623 miles and sometimes as far away as 252,088 miles. On average it's 238,855 miles from Earth to the moon. It took Apollo 11 just under seventy-six hours to make the journey forty years earlier.

'Why does the moon have phases?' he asked.

I showed Sam this one with two coasters as Earth and the moon, and a pint glass as the sun. As best I could, I orbited one coaster around the other, and moved them both around the beer, making a mess of the table. Sam soon got that sunlight illuminates the moon throughout its orbit, but from our position on Earth we see different fractions of it lit.

And of course: 'Does the moon really control the tides?'

Yes, it was the only thing people appeared to agree on. The gravitational effect of the sun and the moon, aligned at both full and new moon, makes our seas bulge, causing high tides for some and low tides for others.

'Whether that means it controls humans,' I said to Sam, 'nobody's really sure. Even though some people, like Brighton's emergency services, reckon it does. Probably.'

We strolled tipsily back across the harbour towards our hotel, waving goodbye to St Mary's churchyard.

I had a surprise for Sam the next morning over breakfast. I showed him a map of the thirteen churches we'd visit on a 15-mile round trip along the Yorkshire coast.

'A sunwalk?' asked Sam.

'Sort of. Though strictly the moon is still in a position where its face is fully lit to some people on Earth. It's still full moon really. So this will be a daytime moonwalk.'

We called ourselves pilgrims as we walked between town-centre churches decorated for Easter and shabby churches hidden down stony tracks. Some we just looked at, some I put my hands on in hope of absorbing something to fix me. A couple we sat in, side by side, and absorbed the musty smells.

I was brought up without the church, other than playing piano at Christmas carol concerts in Waltham Abbey. And before now, I'd never seen a reason for religion. But today's pilgrimage felt somehow calming.

One church we visited stands out for its simple beauty and sad volunteer. It was arranged like an amphitheatre, with two levels of rickety pews curved around the chancel. Everything was wooden and creaked as we looked at it. The elderly lady in the raincoat told us it could hold over four hundred people when full. But today, on a good day, it would attract no more than ten. 'We need more help,' she said. 'We always need more help.'

'I like the community side of religion,' said Sam, as we sat inside. 'It's a shame really that we don't have that any more—places where whole towns come together as one.'

'It's peaceful here,' I replied. 'Really quite serene.'

Sam turned to see me tearful and gave me a hug. He was sensitive in his questioning. My responses were all about Belle, who, thanks to Mark, I now knew was in a happy relationship.

'I think we should keep walking,' said Sam, standing on a creaky floorboard. 'Sounds like we've got a long way to go.'

I'd never seen the Yorkshire coast before. I found it to be fantastically dramatic. Sand, clay, gravel, limestone, chalk and the occasional dinosaur make up its sheer cliffs, whose headlands resemble wise old faces, weathered by the violence of the North Sea. While waves crashed together and erupted in fury, we heard helpless gulls screeching for relief. Inland, hamlets appeared between the shaking grasses, their distant church steeples guiding us towards the bay and back again. The scene, part controlled by the moon, was in constant movement. Every now and then we'd come to a National Trust marker that asked for our help to protect and maintain the area. Today, it seemed, I wasn't the only one needing support.

With each church we visited, I learned more about the significance of the area to religion. And the integral part the full moon plays in deciding the date of the Easter weekend.

In 664AD, Britain was a mess. Roman rule had ended centuries before and Anglo-Saxons were exerting their power, creating small warring kingdoms across the country. In Whitby, in the heart of the Northumbrian kingdom, an abbess called Hilda had formed a synod to bring consensus, specifically on the date of Easter.

Early Christians had held the celebration to coincide with

Passover, the fourteenth day of the first lunar month in the Jewish calendar. But in 325AD, the Romans decided Easter should fall on the first Sunday after the first Ecclesiastical full moon following March 20th, the date of that year's spring equinox.

The debate continued for centuries, with different branches of Celtic and Roman Christianity celebrating Easter on different dates. Things came to a head in 664AD, when half the royal family celebrated Easter as the rest were still fasting for Lent.

The synod decreed that Easter should follow the Roman tradition, with Easter Sunday falling on the Sunday following the first full moon of astronomical spring. Today, we use this same lunar system to choose the date of Easter. Yet we still call the occasion 'Easter', a name which appears to relate back to a pre-Christian goddess of Britain called Eostre, Estre, Estara, Eastre or Ostara—depending on which source you read. And the moon that determines its date is called the paschal moon, which relates to Passover, or 'Pesach'.

Back in Whitby for the final time, our knees throbbing after fifteen miles of walking, I challenged Sam to a final hunt for William Scoresby's crow's nest. One last circuit of a town I'd started to feel attached to. He said 'no' because his body had never experienced such pain. So I limped on alone, like back in January, the full moon trying her best to light the land through the clouds.

I limped and I limped and I found nothing. So I returned to Sam for a final pint before one of the deepest sleeps I'd enjoyed in over six months.

The next evening, going through photos of my April moonwalk, I told Dad the bad news about William Scoresby as he popped his head into my bedroom.

'Odd,' he said. 'It's there somewhere, Rob. But it doesn't matter. How was your walk?'

And then, as I clicked from a photo of Harry plunging his fangs into Sam, the strangest thing happened.

I turned my screen to show Dad the final shot I'd taken in St Mary's graveyard after the Dracula tour. The one I hadn't bothered to line up. It was an image of a gravestone that read:

In Memoriam
William Scoresby
Born at Nutholm Yorkshire May 3rd 1760,
was many years successfully engaged
in the Arctic whale fishery
Died at Whitby 26th April 1829
Also Rev. William Scoresby
Born October 5th 1789
Died March 21st 1857

May

Facing fears

The car park was empty but for a 4x4 with its engine running. Inside sat a grinning man with a bald head. I parked beside him, wound down my passenger window and smiled through the drizzle. 'Adrian?'

'Ahhhh, so you must be the man from the moon. Welcome to Devon, my friend. Welcome to the weekend of your young life.'

In a miracle befitting the time of year, my old Fiesta, so full of good memories, had been raised from the dead. As I sat in the car park, my engine chugging hard, I thought back to what the mechanic had said when he handed me the keys.

'Probably time to let her go soon. Nothing lasts forever.'

To try and let go of Belle, I'd made a decision. I'd moonwalk once a month, every month, for the whole year. I'd go wherever I needed to go and do whatever I needed to do to grow up, move on and become a real man. Even though I still didn't fully understand what that last phrase meant.

For this moonwalk, I'd emailed a paranormal investigator called Adrian and arranged a couple of days' ghost hunting with him in Devon to see if that would help me. Inspired by Bram Stoker's research trips to the harbour below Whitby Abbey, and determined to stop being spooked so easily, I'd found Adrian's website and asked if we could hang out.

I stepped from my car into Adrian's and we shook hands.

'Rob, ghoulishly great to meet you,' he said in a soft voice. 'Would you like a cup of tea to warm your cockles?'

After ten minutes of introductions, I drove behind Adrian to a bed and breakfast in a nearby coastal town. Over dinner, the paranormal investigator told me he'd been living here for the last year. He'd made it his home. I thought we might hang out and talk ghosts, but he seemed keen to sleep. 'Got a big day ahead of us tomorrow, Moonman. And an even bigger night.'

He wished me a safe sleep and left me downstairs, reading books about local legends.

Both online and in person, people had started to call me 'Moonman'. I liked it as an alias; it helped separate me from the broken-hearted young man called Rob. Between moonwalks, Moonman had started to hang around at astronomy events and visit more observatories. He'd sometimes take his mum, who insisted on calling the moon 'Phoebe' and me 'my boy'—even to London's leading astrophysicists. On one particularly special evening, Mum and I enjoyed a close-up look at the rings and moons of Saturn.

Another evening, I went to an event celebrating one of the most anticipated moon books of the International Year of Astronomy. When the author forgot how far the moon was from Earth, I put my hand up.

'On average, it's 238,855 miles away. Though it depends on perigee and apogee really, where the moon is on its elliptical orbit.' I don't think that author liked Moonman.

Back in Devon the next morning, a howling wind woke me. As I pulled open the curtains, I watched it terrorise trees. The distant crash of waves was interrupted by a loud knock on my door, and Adrian's gentle voice saying: 'Breakfast's up, Moonman.'

Over enormous fry-ups—'You'll need a lot of strength for a weekend with me, my moon friend'—Adrian shared our plans.

We'd start with a windy stroll along the seafront before driving onto Dartmoor, a rugged landscape of hills and valleys, where my host was keen to share tales. That night, by full moon, we'd abandon the car and hike up Hunter's Tor above Lustleigh Cleave and hunt for a legion of Romans.

I stopped Adrian. 'Romans?'

'They like to go walking by the light of the full moon. Just like you, Moonman.'

If we survived the hunt, Adrian promised to share local

myths on his Devil-themed pub crawl, something he'd created for people who visit the area. Then we'd drive to Shaldon, a small town overlooking the sea, to have dinner with Terri, a woman who Adrian said was keen to see me. First though, he wanted me to meet his fellow paranormal investigators.

'Ready?' asked Adrian, shoving some toast into his mouth.

'Absolutely,' I said, not ready at all.

Sitting around a thick oak table in a function room of a pub, Adrian assumed a spookier voice than usual, as he drew the dusty curtains. We were left in candlelight. He circled the table and asked us each to introduce ourselves. There was a giant bard with a pointy beard called Jack, a medium called Sofia, a young woman who worked in a café, and a young man whose face was full of piercings. I introduced myself as Moonman and mumbled something about it being a privilege to hang out with people who liked the full moon as much as me.

Adrian smiled. 'It's our pleasure to have you here.'

Then Sofia tried to speak to the dead. I held the table tight as she asked if spirits wanted to say hello. But nothing happened except Sofia telling us there wasn't anyone around today. Adrian finished the meeting with some paranormal sundry items and a to-do list, like updating the website.

Following the evocation, my friend Matt was waiting for us outside, as planned. He'd arrived from Essex just in time for Adrian to drive us across the moorland to Hunter's Tor. Sofia, the mousy medium, joined us. At her request, we pulled up by a spot called Scorhill stone circle. Before I could properly introduce Matt, Sofia had walked off.

'Where's she going?' Matt asked me.

'No idea. Adrian, what's wrong with Sofia?'

Adrian quickly opened his boot, put on some walking shoes, slid a torch into his pocket, put a backpack over his shoulders, stretched his limbs and marched off in pursuit. 'She's sensing something, gentlemen. Follow me and we'll find out what.'

The sun was going down by the time we caught up with Sofia, who was standing beside a jagged stone.

'I feel the presence of three men,' she said.

Matt whispered, 'Me, you and Adrian, right?'

I whispered back, 'I hope so.'

Sofia continued to pace ahead, following the stones. Ten minutes later, she stopped by another one.

'They are here. Three men in black cloaks.'

Adrian nodded. 'Are they looking for something?'

'I don't think they're actually here,' said Sofia.

'They're thought forms?' asked Adrian.

'They're something like thought forms. They're thought that is here. And it's like they're going from stone to stone to stone. Then they stop at what appears to be a stone. But it's not a stone. You see?'

'I see,' said Adrian.

'I see,' I said, seeing very little. 'You see?' I asked Matt.

'See what, mate?'

Back at Adrian's car, I asked Sofia about the thought forms she'd sensed. She couldn't explain who or what exactly she'd experienced, but she believed it could have been connected to the women of the nearby town of Chagford.

Story goes that any Chagford wife accused of cheating would need to undertake four tasks of repentance, to prove her innocence or cleanse her of her 'crime'. After wading through the boggy pool of Cranmere, she'd head to Scorhill and run around the circle three times. A little breathless, she'd need to climb through the great Tolmen stone, which sits in a nearby stream. Finally, the poor woman would be made to lay out in front of the stones at neighbouring Grey Wethers and repent. If the stone she was closest to remained upright, she'd be forgiven. If it fell, it meant she was guilty—and squashed.

'I think I might have been cheated on once,' I told Sofia, who looked dazed. 'But this sounds like a nasty sort of revenge.'

After a quick flask of tea to warm our hands and settle my nerves, we drove to Hunter's Tor. The weather was now friendlier than earlier—chilly but clear. The wind from the morning had died down and left a fine night for moonwalking.

Two months had now passed since that clear moonwalk with Mark in Battle. Work in the marketing agency in Waltham Abbey was becoming more creative and therefore distracting.

While every evening and weekend I was dedicating to the moon. I didn't know whether blocking out pain with new experience was the right way to mend a broken heart. But Belle felt a little more distant than before. Friends, old and new, had gathered around me, like Sam and Matt, to offer more support and advice. The best piece, which only made proper sense to me later in the year, remains this: 'It's not what happens to you that makes you who you are, it's what you do in response.'

By the time we reached the brow of Hunter's Tor, the full moon had risen higher above the hills surrounding us, casting a soft light as far as I could see. The air was still and silent but for the very occasional whinny of a wild pony. I turned on the spot in a full circle, taking in the ragged land and tufts of grass, the pools like tin foil in the light of the moon, the stones piled high like pancakes, Adrian's wide eyes, Matt's confused brow and—

'Where's Sofia?' asked Adrian.

A cold breeze combed the long grass close to us.

'Sofia?'

There was no response.

'Sofia!'

'The Romans?' Matt whispered to me.

'Or the thought forms?' I whispered back.

We moonwalked far that night. The last time I checked my watch, it was 4am. I'd never been out in nature so late, so had never witnessed the shallow arc of the summer moon before.

It acted as our torch, moving with us as we searched with one eye for Sofia and the other for a legion of Romans marching on the tor. Just before dawn, we called off the hunt—for both Sofia and the soldiers. Adrian said he wasn't too concerned about his friend; sometimes she was carried away by spirits and would re-appear perfectly fine later on. Though we were all upset not to prove the legend of Hunter's Tor.

As we got back to Adrian's car, Sofia was sitting inside. Her pupils were pulsating but her body looked relaxed.

'Are you ok?' I asked her.

All she said was she wanted tea, which Adrian poured for her. She drank it in one and asked for another. I never found out what happened to Sofia that full moon. She wouldn't tell me or Adrian. In fact she didn't say another word that night.

Matt stayed with me in the bed and breakfast. In the morn-ing, before he drove back to Essex, we had a proper catch-up.

'Remind me why you're down here doing this,' he said.

'As you know, I've always fought fire with distance. Run away from difficult situations. Denied they're really happening until they're replaced by something else. Well, after what happened with Belle, that's been tricky. So I'm throwing myself into lots of challenges instead. Facing some fears. Becoming a real man.'

'You already *are* a real man,' said Matt. 'A good man. What happened with Belle doesn't make you less of a man. It just makes you... dumped and single. Enjoy yourself.'

I laid back on my bed. 'What I mean is the more active I am, the less time I have to think about what's gone on. The less I think, the more I can pretend nothing's happened.'

'You just said you wanted to confront things. Now you're saying you want to pretend it hasn't happened. It *has* happened, Rob. And that's not gonna change.'

'I guess. But I definitely feel better doing these walks.'

'I suppose that's a good thing then,' said Matt.

'We need to watch out here,' said Adrian, as he drove us across a bridge close to a hamlet called Postbridge. 'I need to hold tighter to the wheel than I normally would.'

He gestured towards his hands, which were bright pink.

'Why's that?'

'It's the Hairy Hands. They've taken the wheel of many vehicles here before. I'll be extra careful for you, Moonman.'

'Sorry, what?'

'Their first victim was a worker from Dartmoor Prison. It was back in 1921. Riding along on his motorbike, all of a sudden this big pair of nasty, hairy hands grabbed his handlebars and steered him off the road into a ditch.' Adrian paused and stared at me. 'To his death.'

'How do they know that if he died?'

'His children were in the sidecar and watched it happen.

They survived. Their father didn't. The moors are full of these grisly tales, my moon friend. Tell you more later. But now I sense a stamp. Do you?'

Adrian pulled his 4x4 onto a grass verge and, similar to the night before, collected equipment like we were going into battle. But instead of a torch, this time he picked up a pad of paper, a stamp with a ghost symbol on it, a compass and a long tree branch. 'Time to introduce you to the ancient art of looking for rubber stamps,' he said, laughing. 'Or letterboxing.'

After an hour or more of watching Adrian prod stones and streams with his branch, I learned that letterboxing is a mixture of stamp collecting and orienteering. People in the know are given coordinates for books and stamps hidden around the moors. When they discover a site, they exchange marks and move on. As we toured the terrain looking for the hiding places, Adrian looked as happy as I'd seen him since we'd met. I started to wonder whether moonwalking might start to become my letterboxing: a regular hobby to keep my mind present.

That evening, on the drive to dinner at Terri's cottage in Shaldon, I fell silent. Maybe it was Matt leaving, or his warning me that ignoring my feelings might not be the best way to heal. Perhaps it was tiredness from late nights moonwalking and long days prodding streams. Whatever it was, I felt as hollow as the Tolmen Stone and as flat as a cheating Chagford wife. Even finding a rare stamp near the Pixie Cave couldn't lift me.

'Are you ok, Moonman?'

It was easiest to say 'yes', that I was just taking in nature.

Adrian's energy continued into the evening, as we drove between three country pubs towards Terri's home. During the pub crawl, Adrian shared the legend of Jan Reynolds, who sold his soul to the Devil in exchange for seven years of good luck playing cards. With intense stares, disturbing sound effects and a couple of bangs on the table, my guide came to life. I could only dwell on my lack of fortune in losing my love.

Outside Terri's cottage on the hill, I admitted to myself for the first time in a while that all I wanted was a kind whisper from Belle to say everything would be ok.

What came next was far more magical.

June

A moment of magic

Something happened to me that evening with Terri.

Nothing spooky, like in Debbie's cellar. Nothing weird, like bumping into James in Walthamstow. And certainly nothing as freakish as that William Scoresby photo. I can't explain what it was. But I'll be forever grateful for it.

Terri was thirty years older than me, had long blonde hair thick with curls, and twinkling earrings that rippled like leaves in a breeze. Her eyes smiled, her cheeks smiled, the shape of her face smiled. If I could have seen her heart, I'm sure that would have smiled wider than everything else. When she asked a question, she listened so closely to the answer she didn't blink. And when she spoke, her words felt soothing and healing.

After dinner, she led me and Adrian down the hill from

87

her home to a stone archway in Shaldon. It was a clear night, although I couldn't see the moon.

'I can hear the sea,' I whispered, looking into a tunnel. 'Where are we?'

'Walk on, Moonman,' said Terri, releasing my hand. 'Just walk on and see what you find.'

The sound of lapping water increased the further I stepped into the darkness. After a few seconds, I couldn't see in front of me any more. I put out my hand to follow the slimy walls until I turned a corner. Like a singer returning to stage for an encore, I emerged below the limelight of the full moon. I stood and scanned from beach to foaming surf to gleaming sea, my eyes slowly rising like I was admiring the most beautiful woman in the world. Her toes then thighs then hips then stomach then breasts and shoulders and, eventually, her most perfect face smiling at me. As I looked up, I saw the distant dimples of Phoebe. Not just a moon but a goddess. *My* goddess.

The light she handed down tiptoed on the ocean surface, creating a path for me. I froze. At that moment, for the first time in over nine months, I felt love again. Not for Belle. She'd vanished from my mind right now, Tonight, I felt an overwhelming closeness to a rock 238,000 miles away, a paranormal investigator, and a woman I'd only known for a few hours.

Adrian appeared behind me. Then Terri, her jewellery twinkling in the moonlight.

'Buddha's path to Enlightenment,' she said, pointing to the light reflected on the ocean.

We stood without speaking.

'We're too late to see moonrise,' said Terri later, her words sailing to sea, 'but if you truly want to connect, to understand, to *be* somewhere, you should see Luna rise from the water.'

Terri held my hand. 'Next month, on the night of full moon, visit a beach where you can see the eastern horizon. The moment the sun disappears, look opposite to witness magic.'

'More magical than this?' I asked.

'Trust me,' she whispered.

On February 6th 1610, Sir William Lower of Trefenty, near the south coast of Wales, wrote the following to Thomas Harriot, the man I'd first heard about at Astrofest in February:

I have received the perspective Cylinder that you promised me…
According as you wished I have observed the Mone in all his
changes. In the new I discover manifestlie the earthshine, a little
before the Dichotomic, that spot which reprefents unto me the Man
in the Moone (but without a head) is first to be feene, a little after
near the brimme of the gibbous parts towards the upper corner
appeare luminous parts like stares much brighter then the rest and
the whole brimme along, looks like unto the Description of Coasts

in the dutch bookes of voyages, in the full she appears like a tarte
that my Cooke made me the last Weeke.

Reading this in Henry Stevens's 1885 biography *Thomas Hariot* soon after my May moonwalk, I smiled at Lower's description of the full moon. I could easily see his cook's cratered pastry. I also enjoyed learning about Lower's close relationship with Harriot, whose character came to life as I studied letters the astronomers had sent to each other.

Harriot (also Harriott, Hariot and Heriot) was born in Oxford in 1560 and later studied there. On graduating in 1580, his fascination with mathematics, astronomy and navigation earned him a role as Sir Walter Raleigh's tutor, teaching Raleigh and his crew the skills they'd need on their journey to establish a settlement in the New World.

In 1585, Harriot himself travelled to the settlement, called Virginia at the time but now part of North Carolina, having learned the Algonquian language from two Native Americans. He later compiled the first historical account of the place, *A briefe and true report of the new found land of Virginia.*

Legend says Harriot was the man who introduced Raleigh to tobacco. While records show he was later locked up in the Tower of London for his family connections to a conspirator in the Gunpowder Plot. Harriot, I decided, was both a fellow moon *and* travel freak. Any friend of his was a friend of mine.

So with a plan to visit Harriot's London residence, Syon House, later in the year, for my June moonwalk I decided to drive to Trefenty, once home to his penfriend William Lower. I wanted to feel part of their friendship. But I had another motive. In Wales, I'd find a beach with a view to the eastern horizon, wait for the sun to disappear, and welcome magic. A rising moon, I promised myself, would make my spirits soar and heart smile. If only I'd checked the weather forecast.

I got to Wales just as a summer storm was thundering across the Irish Sea. I parked at my bed and breakfast, said hello to my hosts, took a walk around the tiny Welsh town I'd be calling home for the night, and headed back onto the road. During my tarot reading, Debbie had mentioned feeling extra energy by full moon. Today, for the first time, I knew what she meant.

In nearby Laugharne, I looked around Dylan Thomas's writing shed, perched above the Tâf estuary. It was here, in the Boathouse, that Thomas wrote some of his finest prose and poetry, including the radio drama Under Milk Wood, so full of moon references.

Thomas's short life was as turbulent as the clouds steam-rollering towards me this afternoon. His marriage to Caitlin Macnamara—a union described as 'raw, red bleeding meat' by his wife—was charged by alcoholism and infidelity. I imagined Thomas found peace here in his writing room, looking out across the water. It must have reminded him of his childhood in the Welsh countryside, where he began to write. Like the 19th-century Romantics who inspired him, Thomas explored his feelings through reflections on nature. He died in 1959 in New York aged just 39. An autopsy revealed he'd been suffering from bronchitis, pneumonia and emphysema. It didn't note his emotional turmoil and likely heartbreak.

Clown in the moon
Dylan Thomas

My tears are like the quiet drift
Of petals from some magic rose;
And all my grief flows from the rift
Of unremembered skies and snows.

I think, that if I touched the earth,
It would crumble;
It is so sad and beautiful,
So tremulously like a dream.

Thomas's body was flown back to Laugharne and buried in a churchyard a few hundred metres behind the Boathouse, to the sadness of Caitlin who later wrote: 'I should feel much happier if he were facing the water that he loved and wrote about in his poems.' As I faced that same water, I completely agreed.

I found it hard to leave the Boathouse. I felt I'd made a friend in Dylan Thomas. But my journey needed to continue.

In a nearby café, I stopped for food and to write my thoughts. There were a couple of hours until sunset, but the sky was now completely cloaked in purples. A young lady about my age, with rosy cheeks and a sparkling smile, served me. I told her why I was in town for the night.

'Even if the sky clears, love,' she said, her lilting Welsh accent as calming as the estuary, 'you're not going see the horizon to the east from here. There's towns and hills and plenty of land in the way. Llanybri, Llansteffan, Llandyfaelog, Kidwelly.' Her words bounced like a bee between blossom.

'Where do you think I should go then?'

'Pendine,' she replied, without hesitation. 'It's a long, long, long beach where you can watch the water all around you. If you don't see the moon there, you won't see it anywhere, love.'

'I'm Rob,' I said, as she walked away.

'Amy. Good to say hi.'

As Amy returned to the counter, the sky exploded. I fidgeted inside the café and slumped as Wales disappeared. After the little happy high of speaking to Amy, my heart fell back down. But I thought about Dylan Thomas, writing through his most challenging moments. 'Rage, rage against the dying of the light,' he wrote in 1947. 'Do not go gentle into that good night.' And there's no way Harriot or Lower would have given up on their mission to map the sky because of a thunderstorm. They'd have waited it out and returned to their cylinders more determined.

I sat back down, pulled out Stevens's biography of Harriot, and tried my best to just accept the situation. Giving up on the magic I'd been promised, I told myself, wasn't an option. Therefore worrying about which way the wind might blow next was just a waste of time.

From what I could see, Harriot's first drawing of the moon wasn't very good. Especially compared to those of Galileo, who managed to map the lunar surface in remarkable detail a few months later. Two-dimensional and vague, Harriot would win no prizes for artistry. But that wasn't the point. Harriot, in regular contact with Lower in Trefenty, had turned his telescope towards the five-day-old moon and begun a series of revelations that would change history.

I reached Pendine Sands just as the light began to fade. The rain had stopped but Nanny Becky's night clouds were everywhere, drifting like oil spills. I stepped from my car into a puddle, the water creeping into my canvas trainer, through my sock and up my trouser leg. With each squelch towards the beach, I felt more dispirited. Near the bay, a plaque told me that Malcolm Campbell had claimed the land speed record here three times. He'd also lost it here twice to John Godfrey Parry-Thomas, who died on these sands on March 3rd 1927, trying to reclaim his record. It was a new moon, when Phoebe casts no light.

Following the rain, mosquitoes had come out in swarms. I took off my sodden trainers to walk along the sand. After ten minutes, I stopped and sat on a smooth rock and covered my feet in my rain jacket. But the bites continued.

I waited. And I waited. And as I waited, flocks of birds flew silently overhead. And as I waited longer, the rumbles of thunder grew faint until all I could hear was a thousand sand hoppers, flitting around me. And I waited and I waited until all of the light of the day had wished me good night, and eventually the clouds above the water had begun to part. And as I waited, I cast my eyes across the horizon, looking for any sign of a glowing white orb, rising. And as I waited I opened my notepad and wrote, without thinking, 'Belle, my once true friend'.

But before I could write more, the sun began to rise over the water. The *sun*—that burning ball of orange that had just set behind me—had accidentally returned. Terri had told me to expect magic but this went against everything I'd learned at the Royal Observatory, everything I'd been reading about astronomy and how the Earth orbited the sun. In fact, everything I knew about science. I'd never seen such an enormous sun. But strangely, as it continued to climb across the sky in its low arc, its fire faded. Within fifteen minutes, it had gone from crimson to salmon to vanilla. In fact—and I wouldn't say this to many people—I remember thinking at the time that the sun now looked a bit like the moon.

On closer inspection, it *was* the moon. It had been the moon throughout, from the moment it had looked huge and bubbling up to now, as it hung delicately in the sky. I held tight to my notepad and cried tears of wonder. My heart danced, my blood warmed, my toes tingled. I couldn't explain why, like I couldn't explain the colours or the size of what I'd just seen. But, as Terri had suggested, something very powerful had taken place.

The next morning, I had breakfast with a cyclist called Glen, who was staying at my B&B. Glen was cycling the coastline of the British Isles, covering over 11,000 miles of hills, valleys and sand hoppers. He was doing it all for charity, and because he'd separated from his wife and wanted to 'do something a bit selfish'. Glen was about halfway through his journey when we spoke. As he loaded up on carbs, I told him about my night on Pendine Sands, and shared stories from my other moonwalks. He offered me a handshake and told me my journey inspired him.

As I packed my car to drive back to Essex, I remembered Trefenty, the home of Sir William Lower, Thomas Harriot's penfriend. I drove around the lanes of Carmarthenshire for over an hour looking for the place to see what else it might reveal, before spotting a tiny road sign with the name on it. Following a narrow track through a half-open gate, I parked close to what looked like a farmhouse and stepped out of the car.

As I crossed the gravel to the front door, three enormous

black hounds bounded towards me from nowhere. I immediately turned and jumped back into the car.

I slammed my foot on the accelerator and left Trefenty before you can say 'perspective cylinder'.

At the end of June, two weeks after the high of moonrise on Pendine Sands, I took a train to Edinburgh to meet Seb. He was anxious about what we were about to attempt.

At no point in the build-up to the MoonWalk marathon around the Scottish city had my friend been convinced it was a good idea. But I'd explained we were doing it for charity and he'd spoken about wanting to join a moonwalk, so he said 'yes'. Even though it was on a new moon.

The day we met in the city, we did a little pub crawl. That turned into an all-nighter with people from our hostel. I only remember one thing from the blur—flirting with a girl for the first time since Belle, and feeling good about myself.

The next night—at midnight—Seb and I stretched on the start line of the marathon. We were dressed in bras covered in two paper plates that had full moon photos pinned to them. Our hangovers meant we were close to vomiting. Twenty miles in, my friend sat on a kerb. He said he couldn't go on and felt like a failure. His knees had locked and he had nothing left. I lifted him up and told him it's not what happens to you that makes you who you are, it's what you do in response.

Hours later still, stretched out beyond the finish line, the sun now above the houses and beginning to bake us through our tin foil blankets, I talked to Seb about half a year of moonwalks.

'Do you think you've learned much?' he asked. 'From the people you've met and brilliantly odd adventures you've had?'

'Awe. Patience. Respect. Openness. That I'm often capable of much more than I realise, physically and mentally.'

'That's some big stuff,' said Seb, ten years my senior.

'We just walked twenty-six miles in bras. With thousands of women and a few blokes. To raise money for people struggling with cancer. It's proving to be a year of big stuff.' .

Seb put his arm around my shoulder.

'And moonrise earlier in the month. It was so moving, Seb.'

'You're doing a huge thing, Rob. It's great. What's next?'

My head pumping and legs starting to stiffen, I sat for a minute to think. 'Something more relaxing. Bit of reflection. But then I'll get straight back out there for some even bigger and odder stuff. I can't wait to see where it all takes me.'

Phase III

Waxing

July

Recharging

On June 25th, the day I returned home from Edinburgh, the world's most famous moonwalker suffered a cardiac arrest and died. His final world tour, 'This is it', wasn't to be.

Michael Jackson's moonwalking was of course very different to mine: a sort of reverse slow-motion floor slide, like when you try to scrape chewing gum off your shoe. But I felt upset at his passing. It left just Neil Armstrong, Buzz Aldrin, a few other astronauts and me as the world's remaining moonwalkers.

In London, a flashmob turned up outside a train station the following evening. I was stuck in the marketing agency doing something dull so could only watch the event online. It looked like thousands of people had got together to sing, dance and re-member this moonwalker in the best way possible. Once again, moonwalking had brought strangers together.

My brother cranked up 'Don't stop til you get enough' on the car stereo as we drove north for a night of full moon fishing. We paid our respects in our best falsettos.

David had always been a keen angler. Me less so. But when I read a theory that animals become charged by moonlight, especially squid, I was hooked—and curious to know more. Plus, I hoped a July night beside a lake might help bring me a little respite in this year of brilliantly odd adventures.

We reached Taverham Mill, hidden from the main roads in a hundred acres of Norfolk countryside, late afternoon. With thunderous clouds once again mumbling overhead, we lugged David's fishing gear along the boardwalk, between the otter-shocking electric fences, past the trickling River Wensum and towards our lake. The earth and sky were sweating.

'Honestly, Dave, at some point in your life, watch the moon rise from the sea. It's enormous and orange. And stupid people would probably think it was the sun.'

With cosmic conundrums starting to bother me, I'd got in touch with a professor back at the Royal Observatory in Greenwich. He said he was happy to answer any of my questions. I asked him why the moon sometimes looks enormous. And, hypothetically, whether it could ever be mistaken for the sun.

The moon illusion makes the moon look bigger the closer it appears to the horizon, he explained. There are many theories why. It's most likely to do with relative size theory, where our eyes size an object based on what's around it. When the moon is high, it appears small in the huge expanse of space, among the stars. When we see it close to our horizon, we compare it to trees, houses, hills and so on. Relatively, it looks huge.

He went on to explain why June's full moon had looked like the sun as it rose from the water. Pink, red, cream. Frazzling and sizzling around the edge. That was to do with the Earth's atmosphere, which is full of particles that absorb and scatter light. Like with a lot of what the professor shared, I didn't fully understand it. But from what I could make out, when we see the moon or sun through our atmosphere, those particles amplify the red part of the colour spectrum.

'Right, come on, bro. Less talking, more walking,' said David, wobbling under the weight of rods, chairs, food, beers and a baitbox. 'We've got clonkers to catch.'

Giant pellets of rain were now piling down.

'How's your head after the puddle incident?' I asked, helping to set up the bivvy and rods.

'Better thanks, bro. Hopefully we won't have any falls this time, eh? Good moonwalk that though. I'm glad we did it. Even though it should have been thirteen miles.'

The more I read about the moon, the more fascinating her role in our lives felt. So many connections, or supposed connections. So much guesswork, so many stories, so much lore. And so many disputes between people of science and people of faith. Educated, qualified, smart people, bickering polar opposite arguments about a distant rock.

My favourite book about the subject was still Arnold Lieber's *The Lunar Effect*, which featured many of the professor's moon studies and theories.

I'd emailed the professor after reading his book the fifth time. He got back saying he'd retired and not done any lunar studies for twenty years. Though he did encourage me to read his second book, *How the Moon Affects You*, which shares another fifteen years' worth of research. Sadly, he told me, analysis of that work had 'failed to replicate the original findings'. He still believed there was a small effect of gravity on human processes. But 'the vicissitudes of space-time, geographical and socio-cultural influences make hard proof unlikely'.

As evening began to approach and the sun's rays became hazy, the lake's surface came to life. Water boatmen met with midges. Damselflies danced. A lone coot bobbed across the still scene. And the bright colours of day, which had dazzled between downpours, melted into dying-ember reds and dusky, dusty pastel pinks. Once-crisp shadows lengthened and lost their edges before becoming one with the leaves of a legion of water lilies. Flowers everywhere, lifting their heads again after the rain, released sweetness. In the sticky air, the scents hung around us. The evening was thick as sauna steam.

'Why exactly are you here with me?' said David, reclining

in our tent. 'You've always said fishing's boring. Or cruel, after Dad accidentally killed that stickleback when he struck too hard... into that wall.'

'I think I said it was for losers... No, I've just been reading about animal behaviour under full moon and it fascinated me. Especially squid.'

David stared at me. 'You realise squid are salt water animals? Probably aren't many in these lakes.'

'I know that. But I guess all fish will behave the same.'

'Not really. Just look at the habits of bottom feeders and surface feeders. You'll find they're all subtly different in how they behave. And surely squid aren't fish?'

Ignoring David, I told him what I'd read about squid. That many fishing boats would prepare for an increased catch by full moon, or turn LEDs to their brightest to lure their prey to the surface, mimicking moonlight. I also told him about Dartmoor's whinnying wild ponies, the howling hound in Whitby and the demon dogs of Trefenty. I'd noticed so much interesting animal behaviour, all under full moon.

'So it's to do with light then?' asked David.

He reeled in and cast back out skilfully, landing his line exactly where he'd told me he would.

Light was one theory. That the full moon reflects more light and therefore more energy from the sun, charging squid and increasing their metabolism, making them hungrier than normal. Though I'd also read that moonlight scares fish to the depths for fear of predators, who can hunt more effectively in moonlight. Then there's the theory that the full moon has no effect on humans or animals whatsoever. It's just a big rock that orbits the Earth.

Over halfway through the year, friends and family would now message me, and more and more drunks in pubs accost me, to demand hard facts about the moon. I felt like Professor Lieber, curious but never fully satisfied by what I learned. Everyone could tell me the moon controls the tides so of course it must affect humans because humans, like the Earth, are made up of so much water. Now, seven months in, I'd respond that often the desire to believe something could be as strong as fact. Sometimes we take as true what we want to believe.

'From what I've read, nobody really knows,' I told David. 'Like with so much else connected to the moon. I sort of like that about her. I like to believe there's more than we'll ever know.'

I took two beers from the tent and we settled in for the evening.

'I think that's the pole star up there,' I said, pointing at a distant twinkle about an hour later.

'Nice,' he replied. 'Where's your full moon? You're not going to make it up again like last time, are you?'

A few hours in and we hadn't had a bite. And we'd only had fleeting glimpses of Phoebe, as the storm clouds passed. These were the days before smartphones had taken over the world. So with little else to do, we reclined in our fishing chairs and shared more beers, nuts and brotherly chats.

'Hear anything from Belle these days, mate?'

I took a sip of beer. 'Not a word. Last I heard, she was studying in Cambridge and maybe marrying someone.'

'Still in love with her?'

I stared out to the still water and breathed a series of deep breaths. It had almost been a year since those six words.

'Um… not *that* sort of love,' I replied. 'We were together four years, so I suppose I still have some loving feelings for her. But something changed recently.'

David handed me a fresh beer. 'That's probably a good thing, eh? Heartbreak always takes time to get over.'

'Ever been heartbroken?'

We'd never spoken to each other before about love and loss.

'Yes, once. It was horrible at the time. Nastiest feeling, like being punched in the gut. But I moved on, met Nat, fell in love again. In fact I need to tell you something about that. Remind me later.'

'What did you do in response to the break-up?' I asked. 'Apparently that's what makes you who you are.'

'I wasted loads of money on a flight to Australia, felt rubbish and lonely, hated it, came back and got on with things. You've only got one life, mate. It's best to enjoy as much of it as possible. Or it just passes you by.'

It was creeping closer to midnight. The moon was a fleeting visitor, low in the sky between the trees that surrounded the tranquil lake, and the temperature had plummeted. David was trying to get a little sleep, wrapped in all the clothing he'd brought, which wasn't much. I stayed awake, writing down my favourite moments of the year so far. Seeing moonrise was top of the list.

I re-cast our lines a couple of times—first into a weeping willow, then behind us, hooking the bivvy. David wasn't pleased when he woke, a bit beery and frozen to the marrow.

'Where's this poxy moon?' he said. 'Every time I do one of these stupid moonwalks with you, the moon doesn't show. And can this even be a moonwalk if we're not walking?'

I stood in a huff, my peace disturbed by the cranky fisherman.

'Ok, fine. I'm going for a walk. A *moon*walk.'

Our fishing spot was surrounded by twigs, branches and great limbs of trees. I could hear my brother tutting as I crunched away from him.

'You're disturbing the fish!'

'What poxy fish?'

The trees became denser the further I walked. And because I'd stropped off, I'd forgotten to take a torch with me. But a strange thing started to happen. The longer I was without light, the better my vision became. Trees began to silhouette themselves, like the moon was lighting the woods. But moonlight had become unmistakeable to me, and this certainly wasn't it. I figured my eyes were becoming pros at exploring after dark.

At the water's edge, I sat with my notepad and opened it to the page I'd titled: 'Belle, my once true friend'. I drew a line through that and wrote just two words in its place: 'Thank you'.

Because I'd realised something. Had Belle not ended our relationship when she did, I might never have pushed myself to have these adventures. Although nights in together with wine and a movie were great, moonwalking was giving me so much more— new friends, knowledge, stories, night vision. Without that Sunday morning almost a year ago, I might never have made time for myself to take this sort of journey. I might not have seen a need.

Back in the bivvy, I found David trapped in a deckchair, giggling. It appeared he'd taken another tumble while I was away. I managed to help him sit up.

'Got some news, bro,' he said, holding the now-cold thermos flask. 'Nat and I are getting married. Did I say?'

'*What*? When? Really? That's brilliant news. Congratulations.'

'Yeah, took her to Paris and proposed. Might have actually been full moon. Let's say it was. Makes me sound more romantic.'

I laughed. 'Such a cliché. A lovely one. But still. You'll need to start thinking about honeymoon soon.'

'I hear moonrise in Wales is nice.'

That night sitting beside Taverham Mill lake, we had no bites except those from gnats. No squid rose to the surface at the moments the moon glowed. No carp or tench nibbled. We didn't even see a stickleback. But it was precisely the full moon I needed—calm, reflective and immersed in nature.

It was now very early morning and felt freezing for summer. I waited until the moon was beaming between the now-tiny puffs of cloud, stood and pointed skywards.

'See that poxy moon? That rock up there is hundreds of thousands of miles from our planet. It stops us wobbling, but keeps us thinking and wondering.'

David looked confused. He was half-asleep.

'Forty years ago today this month, Dave, Apollo 11 set off to try and land humans on that rock. That's amazing, isn't it?

'They circled the Earth to test their spaceship was working before different parts of their rocket, Saturn V, blasted them onto their lunar trajectory. Their path to the moon, bro.' I pointed as high into space as I could. '*That* moon. This month forty years ago we walked on that moon.'

Today, we like to brag that our phones have more computing power than the system that took Apollo 11 to the moon. But the Apollo Guidance Computer was remarkable. Not only did it calculate its position using the astronauts' measurements of the Earth, sun and moon, and therefore compute their course, but it also controlled many parts of the spacecraft, communicating with 150 different devices. It was sextant and project manager in one. Without it, Apollo 11 would never have reached its destination.

'Once more, Dave—humans have walked on that moon. Isn't that mind-blowing? Isn't that crazy and brilliant and wonderful and...' Running out of hyperbole, I just took in the scene.

David reeled in for the final time that night, stood next to me and peered up. 'I wonder if they caught any squid up there.'

August

Respecting nature

On August 25th 1835, the first of six articles appeared in *The Sun*, a New York newspaper. The first headline read:

GREAT ASTRONOMICAL DISCOVERIES
LATELY MADE
BY SIR JOHN HERSCHEL, L.L.D. F.R.S. &c.
At the Cape of Good Hope

It went on to describe how Herschel—son of William Herschel, first president of the Royal Astronomical Society—had used a telescope to spy a menagerie of creatures enjoying life on our moon. There were beavers that walked on their hind legs, enormous blue goats with single horns, giant crane-like birds and half-man, half-bat things, with wings like those of fallen angels. Illustrations showed how they lived in prehistoric valleys, among violent waterfalls and still lakes.

For three weeks, the world questioned how Harriot, Galileo and every astronomer since had missed the fauna that decorated the moon's surface. If life existed in such rich variety there, people wondered, where else might we find it?

But of course none of it was true. The articles had been written by Richard Adams Locke, a reporter at *The Sun*, and soon became known as the Great Moon Hoax. Instead of breaking news that would change humanity forever, Locke—possibly with the help of colleagues—wrote the articles to sell more newspapers. Which they did.

I read this while researching telescopes in the weeks before the August full moon. Although I didn't have the money for anything bigger than a primary school scope, I liked the idea of feeling like an astronomer, making my own observations of the cosmos. So I saved up and ordered one. What arrived a few days later was no bigger than my forearm. It was made of blue-and-yellow plastic, and completely useless. One night I almost saw what the neighbours were having for dinner. But not quite.

The first telescopes used by Harriot and Galileo to sketch the moon, those 'perspective cylinders', were called Dutch trunkes. They'd been created, most likely, by a German-Dutch spectacle maker called Hans Lippershey. Hans at least was the first to try to get a patent for the invention in 1608.

As exciting as it was to discover that Thomas Harriot, a fellow Englishman, had sketched the moon through a telescope before his Italian counterpart, it was Galileo's drawings, published in *Sidereus Nuncius* or the *Starry Messenger* in 1610, that changed the world.

Before Galileo's astronomical treaty, it was commonly accepted that celestial bodies, including the sun, orbited the Earth. A few troublemakers, like the 15th-century mathematician and astronomer Nicolaus Copernicus, had suggested otherwise. But the Roman Catholic Church preached geocentrism and that was that—until Galileo used his Dutch trunke to witness moons orbiting Jupiter. He also produced intricate drawings of the moon's surface, with all its blemishes, contradicting the ancient mathematician Ptolemy and philosopher Aristotle, who had believed heavenly bodies to be perfect and made of quintessence, the fifth element. This caused chaos.

In 1633, Galileo was sentenced to house arrest by the Church for his new ideas. But his drawings of the moon and correct theory of heliocentrism changed the world. *Sidereus Nuncius* had encouraged us to see ourselves as just a part of the universe. Not the centre of it.

I was back in Falmouth a year after the break-up.

The last time I was here, I was scrubbing spilt milk from the carpet of a flat Belle and I had been calling home for the last twelve months. We were preparing to move on together. Well, I was.

It was a tatty place—the central apartment in a block of nine. I remember it vividly for its mould, its tight galley kitchen, and because this was the last place I felt in love. Belle and I slummed it in that flat, living with little spare money but, I'd thought at the time, enough love to get us through anything.

Despite feeling like I was 'moving on', a phrase you hear so often when you tell people you've been dumped, some bad dreams kept playing on repeat. There was the one where Belle's dad walked her up the aisle towards me and gave her hand to the man in the photo I'd seen. The one where Belle's best friend tried to seduce me in front of her mate so that she'd leave me. And the most painful dream of all—the one where, perched on the corner of her parents' dining room table, Belle told me she wasn't in love with me any more.

But I hadn't driven three hundred miles to pine after lost love. Instead I'd spent the last month speaking to a man called John Harris. He was a lunar gardener who practised something called biodynamics. He sounded kindly, quite old, very wise and a little eccentric when we spoke on the phone, so I asked if we could hang out together. John invited me to spend an afternoon with him inside one of Cornwall's most beautiful gardens. I hoped some more time with nature might help me to continue healing. Perhaps change my own perspective:

encourage me to see myself as just part of the world, not the centre of it.

With money low, I'd agreed to cat-sit for a friend in a house three streets away from Cliff Court, an address etched forever in my memory. I'd never looked after cats before and, between you and me, had never been keen on them. They always seemed suspicious of me. The evening I arrived and opened the door, two of the cats bolted and I didn't see them again. The third, a black cat with a very visible ribcage, projectile-vomited over the fruit bowl. I locked the bedroom door that night.

The next morning, I remembered why I liked this town so much. I stepped out of the house into tropical warmth, wandered through a wild garden of palm trees and gunnera, said hello to a bouncing postman with sandy skin, and wandered down a long track which led to the sea. The water was soft and still. I avoided the most direct route to the coast, because that would have taken me past my former life.

After lunch with old friends and a little sunbathing on the beach, I drove north through Cornwall's country lanes, lined by hedgerows and farmland, towards Tresillian House Gardens, where John would be waiting. I'd also managed to set up a real money-can't-buy experience in the Lost Gardens of Heligan for that night. I'd emailed Candy Smit, then wife of Tim Smit, the man who rediscovered the Gardens. Asking a cheeky question, I got a very positive response.

But first moon gardener John, who came to meet me at the front of Tresillian House. He was a stocky man, shorter than me, probably in his early 60s. He offered a warm handshake on one of the hottest days of the year, and led me to the gate of the kitchen garden he'd been looking after for almost thirty years.

As we stepped inside, I felt like I'd walked into Victorian England. The air—a wholesome mix of sun-warmed wood and slightly overripe strawberry sweetness—greeted me. There was a wild earthiness to it, even though John had manicured the flowerbeds, keeping them neat and controlled.

John walked me around the tracks of his garden, stopping every now and then to name a plant or offer me a jolly-looking vegetable. Our pace was as considered as the growth of a seed into a tree. Later, we sat on a bench in the full, powerful glare of the summer sun.

'I've learned from everywhere and everyone,' John told me. 'There are theories I respect from cultures around the world. Some date back to ancient times—the Incas, Aborigines, native North Americans and Romans. They were all in tune with nature. And the moon was integral to every one.'

John's already-rosy face was reddening under the sun. 'It all started with a distant relative of a Sioux Indian who I met at the Chelsea Garden Show when I was a young man like you,' he said. 'I learned about nature and the moon. Have you heard about the moon controlling the tides?'

My laugh echoed within the walls of the garden. 'A few times. The tides affect the plants as well?'

'Like with the tides of the sea, moisture rises when the moon is new or full. That's when I plant anything that produces a crop under the ground. It's first quarter moon for anything that produces a crop above the ground, your corns and so on.

'There's most moisture in the soil at full moon, which is when your crops are taking as much from the ground as they can. This is going to give you your best flavours.

'In the last quarter, I'll take cuttings and prune hedges. I make sure to do everything in agreement with nature. It's all about respecting nature.'

I admitted to John that I still didn't know how to tell whether it was first or third quarter, when the moon appears half full. Or when the moon was waxing or waning.

'In the northern hemisphere, the moon rises on the right,' he said. 'If you see the right side lit, you know you're waxing towards full moon. If it's lit on the left, then you're waning towards a new moon.'

John stood and walked me to his greenhouse, where perfectly misshapen tomatoes whispered how happy they were and how much they wanted me to eat them. They tasted like tomatoes my parents promised used to exist, deeply sweet and succulent.

The tour of the garden continued back outside.

'Nothing you taste here will be like the stuff you get in the shops today. That's not picked in agreement with nature.'

I knelt down and held the stem of a flower.

'What would you like to take with you?' John asked.

'Really?'

'Nature's bounty,' he said. 'Eat it fresh tonight or tomorrow. If you can taste the difference—I'm sure you will, it's all 100% organic—come back and tell me one day.'

Time didn't exist in John's moon garden. His stories sailed me across seas to settlements in North America, and around the world to gardeners who practise similar methods to John. My guide spoke slowly and unambiguously, making important points with pleasing pauses. *Nature*, was his message. *Respect nature and nature will respect you.*

The following evening, I'd feast like a vegan king on the beans, tomatoes, potatoes, seeds, apples and other fruit and veg John had shared with me. But now I needed to say a warm good-bye to my host and dash thirty minutes south-east to the Lost Gardens of Heligan before they closed for the night.

One of Candy's colleagues welcomed me just as daytime visitors were leaving. She gave me a quick tour, before Candy herself popped by, said a brief hello and handed me a map of the gardens. Just as she was about to head home, she turned to me:

'Rob, tonight you may stay as long as you wish. We'll just

wrap the chain around the gate.' And then one final thing. 'There's a photographer staying in the gardens overnight, too. It's unlikely you'll see each other. But if you do...' She didn't finish her sentence.

It was a perfect night for moonwalking: clear, sultry and still. I'd marked three sites on my map that felt appropriate for a moonwalk. The first was a sculpture of a sleeping woman called the Mud Maid, the second a wishing well, and the third an old rope bridge that I thought might make me feel like Indiana Jones. I'd wander the gardens at John Harris speed, taking time to breathe in nature and bathe in sweet moonlight.

Seat of a family of Cornish politicians and gardeners for four hundred years, the gardens at Heligan became overgrown early in the 20th century, when a lot of workers went to fight in the trenches. Tim Smit and a Tremayne family descendent called John Willis began to clear and recover the gardens in 1990.

As Candy left me, I filled my lungs with as much nature as they could handle. As I walked, I reflected on why I felt better outside, doing things like watching moonrise, trekking along dramatic coastlines, even hunting ghosts of Roman soldiers.

I realised it was about perspective—a sort of *self* illusion. Alone and in my head, my troubles seemed huge, like I could never overcome them. But when I thought of them along- side 4.51-billion year old cosmic companions, chalky clifftops holding dinosaur secrets inside, and ancient civilisations, they felt manageable. With so much to wonder at, feeling sorry for myself had started to feel self-indulgent. And quite boring.

Each new step confirmed this theory. As frogs croaked below me and bats circled above, as leaves tickled my arms and midges my nose, as a damp warmth rose from hidden pools, as the sharp bark of centuries' old trees scratched my fingers, and as my moon sprinkled a calmness through the canopy and over me, I felt content and happy.

When I came across the Mud Maid reclining on some earth, I sat and spoke to her for a while. I shared a few moonwalking tales, of course first explaining the concept. She listened to all my stories in great confidence—she's made of rock and plants —and whispered that I should make a wish in the wishing well. Beside the well, which I found thanks to moonlight, I continued the note to Belle that I'd been meaning to finish.

I had the opening line: 'Thank you'. And I added a second: 'Thank you for the time we were in love'.

As my pen carved the words into the paper, each letter seemed to take on a little of the weight of loss I'd been carrying. With this lightness, I tossed a penny into the wishing well and made a wish—that Belle would have a good marriage, and that I would one day let go of her and know happy love again.

Then I walked on, opening my eyes wider than I had on previous walks. I felt I was beginning to allow in more light.

September

And the Lord sent us an angel

'You realise I hated you when we first met?'

Phil spat out his hot chocolate. 'What? Why? Fool!'

'Not for anything you did,' I said, looking to the hills behind the never-ending lake. 'But because you've got the same name as the bloke Belle met while we were in Falmouth. I'm sorry.'

Phil stared at me. 'It's fine. Remind me who Belle is.'

Phil had never known Belle. I'd met him a couple of months after she and I had split up—we'd joined the marketing agency in Waltham Abbey around the same time. For the first few weeks, I could only think how unfair it was of the Universe to sit me next to a Phil. But he soon won me over. He'd do things like get trapped inside the studio photocopier, and fall asleep during creative team meetings. In not long, Phil had become a dear friend who I trusted with my deepest secrets—because

I knew he'd forget them—and, as I was about to discover high on the hills of the Lake District, my life.

It was a cold, breezy day beside Coniston Water. Grey, so lifelessly grey that the ducks and the geese and the swans were still snuggled up and sleeping in their nests. There was such a chill in that breeze, which kept catching damp from the water's surface and finding its way inside my thinly insulated rain jacket. Phil was sitting opposite me in his padded waterproof.

'Remind me,' he said, between sips. 'Why are we in Scotland?'

'We're in the *Lake District* for a moonwalk. I told you I wanted to stop reminiscing and have a proper adventure. Like real men do. You said you wanted to come because it sounded fun.'

To get Phil more interested, I told him what had happened in Heligan. I shared how, once I'd made my wish in the wishing well beside the grotto, I went looking for the rope bridge.

'And?' he asked.

'And what?'

'And what happened next?'

'I got a bit lost,' I said. 'It gets dark at night, especially when there's a canopy of trees blocking most of the moonlight.'

The dark map Candy had given me that evening proved useless without a torch. And every trail seemed to lead in circles.

'So I walked and walked,' I told Phil, as he warmed his hands on his drink. 'And I did all I could to avoid bumping into Candy's photographer.'

'Photographer? Candy?'

'Candy Smit, wife of Tim, told me she'd locked a photographer in the gardens with me. It was such a magical night except for what happened at the end...'

'What. Happened. Fool?'

'I'll tell you tomorrow once we've moonwalked.'

Later we enjoyed dinner in a large, dark, quiet pub with a crackling fire close to its bar. It felt suitable for the theme I'd chosen for the walk. Heading back to our hostel room, Phil crabbed off towards a distant noise.

'Hostel's this way,' I said.

'I know. Party's this way. Let's go dance.'

I stopped and pointed to the hill that would take us to our beds.

'C'mon, Rob,' he said, as distant voices cheered. '*You're* the drunk one. And you just said you wanted a proper adventure.'

With that, Phil tried to scale the wall. When he thudded back down to the grass, he tried to burrow underneath it.

'You're being weird,' I said. 'I'll give you a leg up. You party. I want to be rested for tomorrow.'

'Tomorrow? We're just walking up a few hills. You don't need to prepare for that.' He stood up, wiped off some mud and looked at me like a disappointed child.

As I peered into the sky, the almost-full moon appeared. 'I love Phoebe. Do you like Phoebe?'

'Who's Phoebe?'

'It's what I call the moon.'

Phil put his arm around my shoulder. 'And *I'm* the weird one?'

The playwright Anton Chekhov once offered a famous tip on writing, which I'd had etched into me on my course in Falmouth:

Don't tell me the moon is shining;
show me the glint of light on broken glass

We've seen the prominence of the full moon in literature, particularly horror. But read poetry and you'll also find Phoebe illuminating lines in ee cummings, Sylvia Plath, James Joyce, Percy Bysshe Shelley, Emily Dickinson, Carol Ann Duffy, and of course Dylan Thomas. Since leaning on Thomas's writing desk in South Wales and reading how much he'd been inspired by the Romantic poets of the 19th century, I'd wanted to explore as they would have. Thomas's story had got to me.

There seemed no better place for a restorative hike than the Lake District, where the Lake Poets wandered lonely to try and find themselves. But William Wordsworth felt too obvious for a moonwalk. Instead, I turned to his scribbling sibling, and brilliant author in her own right, Dorothy.

I'd read Dorothy Wordsworth's *Grasmere and Alfoxden Journals* as a student and fallen for her ability to strike a balance between straight description and colour. Her style was a sort of reduced Romanticism. She made the Lakes—a place I'd once planned to visit with Belle, but was now more excited to explore with a friend—sound both tranquil and challenging.

Rereading her diaries for the walk, I noted a few passages where the moon appeared:

Wednesday, October 8th, 1800:
Frequent threatening of showers. Received a £5 note from
Montagu. Wm. walked to Rydale. I copied a part of The Beggars
in the morning.... A very mild moonlight night. Glow-worms
everywhere.

Even referencing William Wordsworth as 'Wm.' endeared me to her. Unlike her brother, she told it like it was, called a glow-worm a glow-worm. Perhaps being less William and more Dorothy might help me process my feelings with logic, I'd thought. Stop me meeting the same fate as Dylan Thomas. I roughly plotted an adventure and brought Phil along.

'"Heard the nightingale; saw a glow-worm",' I read to Phil, as he did his stretches the next morning outside Dove Cottage, once the Wordsworths' family home. 'Isn't that great?'

We began to walk up a track highlighted on my cartoon map of the Lakes, which I'd picked up in the tourist information office.

It was still a little breezy outside, but the autumn sun seemed keen to keep us company until the moon appeared.

An hour in, Phil was again stretching like a yogi, this time against a boulder outside a cave that dripped with slime.

'Leg up. Back straight. Make love to the camera,' I said to Phil, taking a photo and trying my best to keep a straight face.

Phil laughed deep, the way only a young Nigerian man can. I could sense God's proud smile vibrating through his lungs and larynx. 'You're such a joker,' he said, reclining in front of the cave. 'When are we going for dinner?'

As I walked over to him, the smell of damp—a smell I assumed was rising from the grotto but wasn't—tickled my nostrils. 'Soon, I promise,' I said, putting my hand on his shoulder. 'But you need to see moonrise first. It's the most moving thing you'll *ever* witness. I swear to you.'

Three hours into our moonwalk, we were tired and hungry but in high spirits. Although we were yet to see any of Dorothy Wordsworth's glow-worms, the Grasmere to Rydal trek, which dipped and dog-legged and dragged us through bogs and woods and over fallen trees before revealing expansive views of distant waters, was as epic as I'd hoped. The scene was hazy but calm. The occasional whip of wind reminded us we were somewhere a little more wild than the city.

'So what happened with your ex-?' asked Phil. 'You don't have to tell me. Though I'll probably forget anyway.'

'One day she said she wasn't in love with me any more and left me. That's it really. Got dumped, trying to move on.'

I had Dorothy Wordsworth's *Grasmere Journal* in my hands.

'Fair enough,' said Phil. 'Found yourself anyone new?'

'Nah, not really bothered about that. Too busy.'

'With the moon?'

'Exactly.'

I imagined Dorothy wandering the same tracks as us, sitting and taking in the views across the hills and lakes.

We walked in the twilight, and walked till night came on. The moon had the old moon in her arms, but not so plain to be seen as the night before.

I'd read this phrase a few times, *the old moon in the new moon's arms*. It took me a while to realise it described Earthshine, a phenomenon where—during a crescent moon, at around the time of sunset—sunlight reflects off the Earth's surface and illuminates the whole of the moon, meaning we see not only the fingernail, but her full face appearing faint. It was first understood and explained by Leonardo Da Vinci in the 16th century, giving it its other name: the Da Vinci glow.

'Up there,' I said to Phil, pretending to spot a path to the top of a steep hill. 'We just need to climb up there and as the sun sets in the west, we'll see the moon rise in the east. I'm sure Dorothy must have walked this many times. Probably to see moonrise, too. You'll love it. It will blow your mind.'

Night hadn't yet come. It was clear though the earlier smell of damp had thickened a little. I could now taste it on my tongue.

I slapped my friend on his shoulder. 'Come on. Let's do it.'

Phil stopped. 'I don't want a dangerous adventure. My girlfriend will be furious if I come home dead.'

'Trust me. I've done eight of these walks. They always work out wonderfully. Except the one in London... and Birmingham... and... Something unforgettable always happens and we celebrate with good food and drink. You've got a girlfriend?'

'I won't if she finds out about this.'

Phil, bless him, followed me. As clouds began to knit the evening sky together and the temperature dropped and the light darkened and the blue turned purple and the birds left like torpedoes from a submarine and something wet and possibly forecast but definitely ignored by me hit my cheek, I grinned. 'Blow your mind.'

The only thing blowing Phil's mind three minutes later was a strong south-westerly. The calm autumn day on the Lake District's hills had descended, very quickly, exactly as we'd been warned in the tourist information office, into a squally shower. The views across the lakes and fells had turned to rain. Raging rain. The sky had darkened and we had no idea where we were. Our phones had no signal, our clothes no waterproof quality any more, our torch batteries no charge, and our cartoon map of the trail no value.

'I'm sorry, Phil,' I said to my friend, who'd gone silent. 'Maybe we shouldn't have climbed this fell. Maybe the local expert lady was right about... everything.'

The wind tore the map from my hand.

'Let's go up here! The moon's up here! It'll blow your mind! You're a stubborn man, Rob.'

'That's what Belle used to say.'

'Maybe you should have listened to her!'

'Phil, I think we should go back now,' I said, looking at the wall of rain around us. 'I'd like to go back.'

'Nice idea, Rob. Where is back?'

I did a three-sixty. 'Don't know.'

The horizon had been consumed by the rain and the clouds. Night had defeated day. The air was so thick with moisture that breathing became a struggle. Visibility was down to zero.

I started to walk.

'Where are you going?'

'To find help. I feel bad. I'll get us out of this.'

'Come back,' said Phil. 'We need to do this together.'

Phil was right. It was silly to think I could rescue us alone. I hadn't really shown at any point that I was a great navigator or adventurer. My mind wasn't there while I walked aimlessly along. Then, as I took one more step into the unknown, Phil ran up behind me and grabbed my shoulder.

'Fool!' He was far more serious than I'd seen him. 'You. Are. A. Complete. Fool! Stop! Look—!'

He pulled me backwards until I fell onto my backside.

'See the difference in colours?'

I crawled forwards a little and looked where he was pointing.

'The black bit that goes on forever is a big hole that you don't come back from. The rest is the rain and cloud the woman warned us about. I told you we should have listened.'

'I'm colourblind. So no, I can't see the difference between the total darkness and the almost total darkness. I'm sorry.'

'You're so stubborn,' said Phil, sitting next to me.

Soon a figure approached through the rain. It was a middle-aged woman in running gear. She was dripping wet but glowing. 'Hello,' she said, calm. 'Are you all right?'

'No,' said Phil. 'No. We're very lost. This fool who likes the moon took us up here to see something magical'—he stared at me for a second—'and now we're lost.'

'We're not lost. We just don't know where we are.'

The jogger jogged on the spot. 'Rydal's over there,' she said. 'Fairfield's up there. Grasmere's down there. That's where I'm going. But I'd better run. Weather's turned. Enjoy the Lakes.' And she was gone.

Phil took a long look up to the heavens before pulling me by my elbow to a path that eventually led us back to a road we recognised. There, walking side by side, he laughed and he laughed and he laughed.

'What's so funny?'

'I prayed,' he said.

'You prayed?' I wiped water from my brow.

'I prayed,' said Phil. 'I prayed for our safety. I prayed for our lives. And the Lord sent us an angel.'

Back in the hostel, drying out, we were scoffing sweet 'n' sour chicken like we'd just been introduced to it.

'Hey. Sorry for being stubborn,' I said. 'Something I need to work on. And thanks for stopping me falling into the hole. You're not as bad as your name suggests.'

'I'll be honest with you,' said Phil. 'I didn't know what to expect from a moonwalk but I can honestly say that Scotland is beautiful.' He laughed. 'Oi, what happened on the rope bridge in the garden last month?'

'Well I eventually found it and it wasn't very impressive at all. Then, as I stepped on it, it shook all over the place, alerting a load of birds, which made me yelp.'

'And what happened next?'

'As the birds flew away, there was this huge flash in the sky. So I sprinted to the gate and drove off. It must have been—'

'The photographer?'

I stopped chewing and thought back.

'Ha! Yes. Didn't think of that. I wondered if it was the moon angry with me for something. Photographer makes more sense.'

Phil stuffed more chicken into his mouth. 'You're such a fool.'

Phase IV

Full

October

Learning to accept

Summer had passed. The days were getting shorter and I'd started to feel conscious there wasn't much of the year left.

I knew I'd come a long way since those first steps through the Greenwich foot tunnel in January. I'd lost a little weight from all the walking, and gained calf muscles that would have impressed Mark. Physically I'd got fitter and leaner throughout the year. But my emotions weren't so constant. They seemed to wax and wane like the moon.

On a lunch break in Waltham Abbey, I bumped into Debbie outside White Witch. She was holding a leaflet for a full moon ceremony in Glastonbury. Apparently a moon goddess would be there. It was lovely to see Debbie and chat briefly about my travels. I asked her if she thought time with a moon goddess would be good for me.

'Only you can find that out,' she said, running back inside to serve a customer. 'Come tell me your stories soon please, Rob.'

I made a promise that I would.

A week later, I drove three hours south west to Glastonbury. Each year, a music festival swells the town's population from around 9,000 to more than 200,000 people. But this Sunday morning it was calm and quiet on the streets. The air was nicely warm and smelled like White Witch.

I walked past the town hall and noticed the doors were open so turned around and went inside. A bearded man in a pixie hat greeted me, putting both of his hot hands around one of mine.

'Welcome to the Faery Fayre,' he said. 'May I ask how you heard about us please?'

'I'm staying here for the full moon and was walking past and heard lots of chatter so I thought I'd—'

'A curious soul,' said the man. 'Come on in, young sir. You'll find a lot of art and books and wonderful people very happy to speak to you about Phoebe.'

He was right. And unlike at Astrofest, I felt comfortable among the kind-hearted folk of the Faery Fayre. There were towering men with giant staffs, wide men with glittery tattoos, tall and short and fat and thin women, very young and very old, in stockings, and wearing delicate wings on their backs. There was such laughter and gaiety, so many friends together. I knew nobody but sensed a shared energy. And I felt confident that everybody in the hall would be aware that it was full moon. Of course they were. Crystal and Magenta and Tinkerbell and Ricardo and all the other people I spoke to. They knew the phase, they knew some lunar legends, and they felt the influence of Phoebe's fullness.

The Faery Fayre was, in a word, joyous. But I wasn't here for fairies. I'd come to share my feelings with a moon goddess and see if she had the powers to make me completely happy. But for that, I'd need to wait until the evening.

Leaving the town hall, I spoke to the man in the pixie hat again.

'This might sound naïve,' I said, 'but is Glastonbury also called Avalon? I've read that it's connected to the Arthurian legend.'

'Have you visited the Tor?'

'I haven't. What's that?'

'*That* is Avalon. When these lands, the Somerset Levels, were covered by water in ancient times, the site of the Tor would have been an island. In the 12th century, the monks of Glastonbury Abbey discovered the coffin and remains of King Arthur and Guinevere there. If true, which I like to believe it is, then Glastonbury Tor is the Isle of Avalon.'

The man in the pixie hat shook my hand. 'Truth can be much more magical than fiction, young sir.'

I headed straight to Glastonbury Abbey and walked around the Chalice Well. In perfect peace, I drank some water from a still pool—some say it's made red by the rusty nails used to crucify Jesus Christ, others say it's coloured by the actual blood of Christ, which spilled from the Holy Grail which Joseph of Arimathea buried beneath the site.

William Blake, a contemporary of Dorothy Wordsworth, wrote the poem 'And did those feet' about Christ's supposed visit to Glastonbury with his disciple Joseph.

During the afternoon, I enjoyed Blake's green and pleasant land, strolling idly through the town and across fields, and generally getting nicely lost. I came across a hawthorn on Wearyall Hill covered in notes written by people from around the globe. I later learned the local legend, that Joseph of Arimathea had travelled back to Glastonbury after the Crucifixion and stuck his staff into the ground here before falling asleep. The staff had once belonged to Jesus. When Joseph woke, it had grown into a hawthorn tree. I liked Joseph's dedication to the man who offered him hope. I liked the actions he took to show respect.

Not far from Glastonbury is the ancient sun worship site Stonehenge. *New Scientist* had spread a rumour the year earlier that this stone circle might also have been used to demonstrate the movements of the moon:

Lionel Syms of the University of East London has proposed that the building of Stonehenge marked a fundamental shift in society from hunting to agriculture, which corresponded with a shift from lunar to solar worship. By combining observations of the sun and moon, our ancestors could have been demonstrating that they were part of the same spiritual force.

Spiritual force. A phrase that would have once meant nothing to me now felt as normal as talking about a 'healing heart'. In old England, surrounded by pagan worship sites, trees of religious pilgrimage, leylines connecting energies and people dressed as wizards, witches and pixies, I wanted to believe there was something bigger guiding me.

I wasn't too bothered if it was earthly or otherworldly, masculine or feminine, something my friends and family might tease me for or not. That didn't matter any more. Mumbo-jumbo, hocus-pocus? As I walked back into the town centre to meet a moon goddess, I cringed at what I'd said to Debbie during my tarot reading. Going to a full moon ceremony now felt as normal as a couple of pints in my local pub. But, I was about to find out, it really, really isn't.

Sitting on the top step outside the moon temple—a yoga studio above a jewellery shop—I bit crescents from my fingernails. Moments before going inside, I felt nervous I'd say the wrong thing, address the moon goddess by the wrong title, bow at the wrong time or forget to bow completely and question whether you're even supposed to bow to a moon goddess. Her seven or so other guests appeared more composed, except one woman who sat in a daydream at the bottom of the staircase. She had her head in her hands.

When a girl in her late teens dressed in a flowing shawl opened the doors, I stepped into the half-light and picked up a cushion, as instructed. Sage sticks were cleansing the air.

'Are you the goddess?' I whispered.

She didn't speak, just showed me to my place on the floor.

After a few minutes of silence and some guided breathing, she began to hum. One by one, others joined in until the room sounded like a beehive. Soon, we were encouraged to close our eyes and take a series of deeper breaths and allow thoughts to come and go without judgement. The humming soon returned, louder now, and became chanting. The sound swirled around my head and eventually inside my chest.

But I was tense. So tense that when the girl placed her hand on my shoulder, I opened my eyes and released a yelp.

'Come,' she said, taking my hand and leading me through a sequined curtain. 'Wait here.'

I could hear a voice through another silken sheet ahead of me. A woman. She was weeping, her breath tugging at her lungs. Another voice—slower, more controlled, female again—responded to her. Most of the words stayed behind the screen. But I made out 'cancer' and 'weeks' and 'my boy'. A moment later, the lady who'd been sitting at the bottom of the steps emerged. Tears rolling down her cheeks, she returned to her cushion on the floor. The chanting continued.

'Please, come,' said the voice from through the curtain, now speaking to me. 'Tell me why you are here.'

I took a step forwards and met a woman whose face was hidden behind a veil.

'Hello,' I said. 'How are you?'

She asked for my hands.

'Hello. Welcome to the Moon Temple. What is your name?'

'It's Rob, though some people call me Moonman.'

'Please tell me why you have come here today, Moonman.'

I went silent, thinking about what I'd just heard. 'It's nothing, really. Just a bit of heartbreak. Nothing serious. I don't want to waste your time.'

'We all have our personal challenges,' said the woman. She held my hands lightly. 'Each is important to us in its own way. Some we must confront. All we must accept. How has your heartbreak moved you?'

I told her about moonwalking.

'You have spent your year wisely,' she said. 'And if you could achieve one more thing by the end of your year, what would that be?'

Without thought I said, 'I'd like to let Belle go. Completely.'

'For that perhaps you need to return to the place where you last shared love with her. Say goodbye and wish her well. Then continue on your path.'

I later learned that the woman behind the curtain wasn't the Moon Goddess but her priestess, a gateway to the Goddess. From what I understood, it was her role to carry messages to the Goddess. By placing her hands on me, the priestess was channelling a little of the moon's spirit into me.

Following the ceremony, I found the woman I'd seen crying, Lily, sitting back at the bottom of the steps outside the temple. She was writing into a notepad.

I asked her if she was ok. She told me she'd travelled hundreds of miles to Glastonbury to spend time with the priestess. She'd been diagnosed with cancer and recently been given just weeks to live.

'I wasn't looking to be healed,' she told me. 'For me, the moon has such positive energy. To share my story with her, I was hoping to accept what's happening to me and to move forwards.'

'And has it helped?'

She turned to me, her eyes watery, but there was a slight smile on her face. 'I think it has,' she said. 'I feel a little lighter. Tell me about you.'

I shared my own story with Lily.

'That's hard, Rob. I can see why you've felt so hurt. But it's the past now and you can't change it. Start living in the moment again. Enjoy as much of life as you can.

'Put your everything into what you're doing, Rob. Live every single second you have. That's how I try to live now.'

Lily's story had moved me deeply.

Walking back along the wall outside the Chalice Well, I looked up for the moon, my rock, but for the first moonwalk in a few months she wasn't there. Feeling alone, I worried for Lily and her family. I struggled to imagine what she must have been thinking.

It would be easy to give up, I thought, whether you were losing your own life or the life of the person you love most. But then I thought back to Lily's slight smile and the acceptance she spoke about. Neither of us believed she'd been healed this evening. And the woman in the veil behind the curtain never suggested that was why she was there. But in sharing her situation with a stranger, it seemed Lily had gained some strength. Her suggestion to start living in the moment stayed with me.

A badger, sniffing along the stone wall in front of me, took me from my reverie. I'd never seen a badger before and tried to feed it a cereal bar. This just spooked the poor creature.

Walking the other direction was a young couple in loose clothes and with nothing on their feet. They were smoking something fragrant, while smiling and chatting. They strolled down an alleyway, holding hands. If anyone knew where to find the Isle of Avalon, it was going to be these two. So I followed.

As I moved from lamppost to tree to car, stepping so delicately that I doubted I would have disturbed a butterfly, I heard my name shouted from behind me.

'Rob. Self. Pierson. Well bloody hell. What are the odds?'

The young couple turned, saw me half-hidden beside a Land Rover, and disappeared into darkness.

'Hello, sir, how on earth are you? And, more importantly, why are you prowling around Glastonbury at night time?'

'Martin?' I said. 'What are *you* doing here?'

Martin, a friend from Falmouth who'd once acted in a student drama I'd written, told me he was in town with his girlfriend.

'Thought we'd take a drive up, have a look around. I've always liked it in Glastonbury. Who were you stalking?'

We stood on the street corner sharing stories of our last couple of years. My loss of love, his new love. My moving back to my parents' house, his moving to a magical cottage in nature. But I said that things were getting better. New friends, new adventures, a relationship with the moon had made me feel stronger. And I told him I was going back to Falmouth next month to accept what had happened with Belle. I also said this was the third big coincidence of my year, and that any more and I'd get suspicious my friends had set this whole thing up.

Wishing Martin a good night, I followed his pointing finger towards a clearing he promised would lead to Glastonbury Tor. I walked up winding tracks, beneath thick night clouds and through a cold breeze, to the tower at the top of the hill.

I'd reached the Isle of Avalon. There I sat beside the crackling embers of a dying fire and wrote the rest of my note to Belle.

It was time to say a final goodbye.

November

Walking the path

I'd received a special message.

Learning that I was returning to Falmouth on full moon, a group of women moonwalkers had invited me to take part in a ritual.

The email said I was welcome to sit with them on a beach and contemplate under the light of the full moon. The women were keen to meet the moonwalking man. But I was only allowed to go if I promised something: that I'd *never* share with anybody the precise location of their piece of coastline. Some things, they said, are too precious and personal to give away.

The invitation was full of charm and I felt excited to meet fellow moonwalkers. But my main reason for returning to Falmouth was that I knew, deep down, I had to let go of Belle. Completely. And this was the only place to do it.

On the cushion inside Glastonbury's moon temple the month before, when I'd been encouraged to spend time with myself, to allow thoughts to come and go, to reflect but not to dwell, I'd struggled. Maybe it was the humming and the chanting from the other people in the room, but I couldn't settle—I couldn't comfortably sit with my own mind and keep focused.

However, later that evening, sitting in silence against the tower at the top of Glastonbury Tor, my mind had begun to process what had happened to me at the temple. Especially the moment Lily had opened up about her prognosis.

Life, I began to see, is full of things we can't control: the weather, the tides, other people's actions and feelings, and life shocks like Lily's. Some things have the potential to devastate us: to make us feel powerless, pathetic, so full of self-loathing. It's easy to allow them to drag us into the depths, and to let the feelings they create reshape who we are. But, as the shy full moon continued to puff clouds across the sky that night on the Tor, I finally understood that we're neither the things that happen to us nor the emotions they create.

That short conversation with Lily had put so much into perspective. That this young woman—faced with a terminal illness, with saying goodbye to her husband and child forever, with knowing how much of their lives and her own she would miss— could show such strength and stoicism. That she had travelled so far to look for a way to move forwards.

In visiting the temple, in confronting and accepting, Lily had gained as much control as she could. To me, that is what defined her. This woman was as strong, brave and determined as anybody I'd ever met.

For too long, I realised I'd been identifying with what had happened to me the day I'd been dumped, and the hurt it had caused. In saying to Belle I'd become a real man, I'd then started a nasty narrative that told me I wasn't a good enough person. This played over and over again until it became a spiteful and destructive addiction.

But no. It had to stop. Tonight I would take back my own control and stop letting that morning define me.

That's why, walking along Falmouth's high street, knowing later I'd climb the hill to the flat I'd once shared with Belle, I told myself I was not only a real man, but, like Matt had said that morning in Devon, a *good* man. Somebody whose friends would travel hundreds of miles, risk injury, dress up in moonbras, to spend time with. Somebody whose curiosity and opened mind had introduced him to a collection of people as wonderfully exotic as the creatures in the Great Moon Hoax. Somebody who refused to give up, even when it was the easiest thing to do.

And it was working. As I ducked into my old local, where a group of men were singing sea shanties in happy harmony, I ordered a pint with a smile, and chatted with a rosy-cheeked drinker wearing a tatty flat cap.

'Full moon's *tonight*?' he asked.

'Yep. Do you like the moon?'

'No,' he said, splashing his pint of ale on the bar.

'Oh. Why's that?'

'I do mad things at full moon. Wondered why I was feeling so emotional today. Should probably be indoors.'

'If you have time, try going for a moonwalk,' I said. 'Phoebe's great when you get to know her properly.'

The night was breezy and streaked with long clouds. I wandered towards the secret beach, keeping close to the coastline. I passed Gyllyngvase, Swanpool and Maenporth and walked on before eventually coming across the moonwalkers, huddled together by a grass verge. I introduced myself as Moonman and was asked to say a few words about why I was there.

'You're the first man we've ever invited into our group,' said the leader, placing her hand on my forearm. 'It's my dad's birthday today so we're dedicating this moonwalk to the men in our lives. Men who are so special to us.'

'I'm honoured. Thank you.'

Those were the last words we spoke for hours. The sound of voices was replaced by the rush of wind through the trees and grasses, and the crashes erupting from the wintery sea. Without torches, we climbed carefully down the steep hill to a stony beach, often reaching out to stop one another from tumbling. On the pebbles we separated, and each walked to a part of the shoreline where we felt comfortable.

My eyes soon adjusted to the dark, until I saw a perfectly spherical cream-coloured stone to sit beside. There was no moon in the sky yet. Night clouds were numerous. But I felt an energy, knowing there was a full moon.

The first minutes of contemplation on the beach I found tricky. Cold and restlessness caused an itch I couldn't scratch. But as time passed, I settled, until I felt a deep calm inside me, and a focus. Countless thoughts drifted by like the clouds above—some happy, some sad, some easy to place, some a little more mysterious. I did my best to accept them all and to allow them to pass with little more than a nod.

My breathing slowed as breaths felt like they were rising from deeper within my chest. The more I focused on breathing, the less tension I felt in my shoulders, my back, my knees; even my hands, which so often this year I'd caught clenched in reddened fists, were loose on my thighs.

Later, I sensed somebody move to another spot on the beach, perhaps to realign themselves with the shy moon. In the past, a disturbance like this might have annoyed me. But this evening nothing mattered enough to cause me anger. As the pebbles rolled over one another, the sounds skimmed across the sea.

I was there. I was totally there. Hearing the waves, feeling the spray on my face, the chill in my fingers, but I was also in a place much calmer. A place where nothing upset me—as long as

I kept my focus and allowed thoughts to move on.

Some time later still, a hand touched my shoulder and I opened my eyes. As my sight adjusted, I saw my fellow moon-walkers, one by one, lifting their bodies from the stones. I noticed how the clouds had changed direction, now sailing over our heads instead of along the horizon.

As we began to leave the beach, Phoebe appeared, more watery than usual. I wondered whether she'd been sharing my journey throughout the year, secretly helping to carry my hurt.

Below her lay a path I was now ready to walk.

Looking up the hills that would take me to the old flat, I turned around and popped back into the pub. Just for one more pint.

The same man from earlier in the evening spoke to me. He was clearly a few more beers in. Within seconds, he was telling me about his wife, who'd recently left him. He began to cry.

After a strong handshake with the stranger and plenty of consoling words shared, I left the pub and began to climb the hills towards Cliff Court. I walked slowly, passing the second-hand shop selling vibrators, which had always made Belle laugh. I stopped and looked at the Oddfellows Arms, a pub that appeared so unwelcoming from the outside that I'd only ever gone in once. To celebrate Belle's new job.

I walked around the bend in the road so tight my old car

could only make it in five movements. Belle's car could do it in three. I walked up Pikes Hill, where I used to chase Belle, making her giggle. I always caught up with her by the wild rosemary, where we'd pick herbs for dinners we enjoyed cooking together. On the hill, wrapped around each other, I'd stop Belle to tell her I loved her.

I reached the path that led to our old flat and breathed deep. After a minute, I followed it to the front door. Cobwebs still knitted the doorways of numbers four, five and six. Our old washing line still hung loose and useless above the overgrown courtyard two storeys below.

I stood on the doormat Belle and I had bought together and left at the flat with our relationship. The lights were on inside number five. It sounded like a couple were watching TV and laughing. Though that might have been the walls.

I remember the exact layout of that flat. I remember the texture of its cheap carpets, its damp smell and furry, green wall patches. I remember so many times looking out of the picture window down to Falmouth's harbour and thinking how much I loved this town; how lucky I felt to be studying here with the girl I was in love with.

Belle and I only met again once after we split up. It was at her parents' house, at the table where roast never happened. I hadn't seen her arms and legs crossed like that before, or her face so void of warmth and character. Her words were taps on a typewriter: mechanical, functional, I suppose necessary. I still learned a lot in our short time together that evening.

She hadn't been in love with me for six months, she said.

But she didn't want to leave me before I'd finished my course. She respected me too much to ruin my studies.

But she resented me, she said, for taking her to Falmouth, into my world, away from her own.

Falmouth had never felt like the right move to her, she told me. It had never become home to her like it had to me.

And of course, I see now, she was perfectly within her rights to say everything she said, and to feel everything she felt. During our year away from friends and family, I hadn't noticed her loneliness because I was too busy.

As I was learning how to build characters and create conflict in stories, I'd missed the conflict growing inside the most important character in my own life. And between her and me. While I made friends and worked with actors and started a theatre company, Belle gave up on our future together.

Looking back now, I admire how composed she was that last time we ever saw each other. Mature, measured, strong. But standing outside the flat this November night, the memories of our life together still vivid, I had to reach deep. I closed my eyes and focused again, allowing the feelings to come and go.

Her appearances throughout my year—drifting out to sea during my mad moment in London, dancing in the moonshadows of Battle, imagining her father handing her to the wrong man at the altar—eventually trickled away like they were water in a stream.

That night in Falmouth, I found myself feeling lighter, happier. Leaving the old flat, my backpack slung over my shoulder, I saw Phoebe smiling down. I said goodbye and wished Belle well.

I was ready to take on my final moonwalk, as comfortable being me as I'd felt in a very long time.

December

Madness and wisdom

I knocked at the front door and waited, excited by what I'd managed to set up. A couple of minutes later, the hallway lights came on and the door opened to a tall man with a wispy grey beard and sparkle in his eyes. He shook my hand, pulled me indoors and shoved a bottle of beer in front of me.

'Welcome, young man. Thought you might need a brew in preparation for tomorrow. Get that down you.'

In Geoff's living room, I shared stories of moonlit mishaps in London, semilunar pen nibs in Birmingham, and talked in detail about my year of very odd coincidences. He started to chuckle.

'When you got in touch and said what you were doing, I thought you sounded completely daft. So I had to say yes.'

'I'm glad you did. This is my last moonwalk of the year. It needs to be a special one.'

Geoff opened a chest of drawers and got out a tatty Ordnance Survey map of Devizes, the town where we'd spend the night, in the house where Geoff lived with his wife. It was also the place we hoped to return to after tomorrow's moonwalk. He unfolded the map until the size of the next day's challenge revealed itself.

'This,' said Geoff, 'is Salisbury Plain. We'll be crossing it.'

The towns in red circles, with names like Clungstow and Dollop, were our markers. 'Mainly because they have good pubs,' said Geoff, taking a mighty glug of beer. 'Why you laughing?'

I was leaning over a kitchen table, looking at a map that meant nothing to me, drinking beers with a man I'd never met before and had only emailed a few weeks earlier, planning a very long moonwalk across Salisbury Plain in the middle of winter with storms forecast attempting to retrace the steps of a group of most-likely fictional smugglers.

'I like that you called me *daft* and not *mad*.'

All year I'd been hearing the word 'mad'. Dad had thought Nanny Becky mad for her heat spots and night clouds, words I'd found were useful for describing a year of walking at night in nature. Mum had told me I was mad for going to Birmingham in a snowstorm; I preferred to think of myself as 'adventurous'. The Falmouth man who'd separated from his wife had told me he did mad things by full moon. Looking back, I wondered if his madness was instead an intense emotional assault.

I'll tell you what *is* mad though, apparently: walking a marathon with a hangover, climbing a mountain without a proper map, sharing my most sensitive secrets with a moon goddess, sitting on a secret beach with a dozen strangers. According to most people I spoke to, other than those who had joined me on a moonwalk, these were the actions of a madman.

So what does a madman do for his final moonwalk of the year? He looks for the weirdest piece of moon lore he can find and asks a stranger to walk with him.

'Looks disappointingly simple to me,' I said, finishing my beer.

'You won't be saying that when we reach the firing range.'

'Firing range?'

The Moonrakers were a group of smugglers who'd lug contraband alcohol from the south coast of England to the centre of the country across Salisbury Plain. Their most retold story, in Wiltshire at least, took place one full moon night in Devizes.

Having deposited their haul in the town's pond a few days before, they returned with rakes to snag their barrels of brandy. They cast their rakes out into the Crammer like fishermen. One, two, three times. But the barrels proved difficult to catch. Focused on their prize, the smugglers didn't see a group of excisemen approaching.

'And what have we got here?' I imagine they asked.

You can picture the look on the men's faces as they quickly thought up a story: something so rich and so cunning that it would throw the tax collectors off the scent.

'Why, we're raking cheese from this here pond,' said the men, pointing at the moon's reflection on the water's surface.

'You're doing what?'

'See that great ball o' cheese there?' said a supposed bumpkin, while his colleagues continued to rake. 'We're tryin' to get it.'

The excisemen guffawed at the idiot locals and left them to it.

In telling the story to English antiquarian and writer John Yonge Akerman, a local shepherd later recounted: 'Zo the excizeman 'as ax'd 'n the question 'ad his grin at 'n ... but they'd a good laugh at 'ee when 'em got whoame the stuff.' Which I think translates roughly as: 'Who are the *real* idiots?'

Geoff had invited a friend on the Moonraker trail with us. His name was Stu and he was a giant.

We stepped off the bus at a town called Orcheston. It was late morning but the sky was dark. Wind tore through the air, causing angry clouds to collide like dodgems.

'How long have you been a rambler?' I asked Stu.

'Long distance walker,' said Geoff, serious. 'Ramblers are *very* different people. We're long distance walkers. Don't make that mistake with anyone else or you won't be around long.'

'Long distance *moon*walkers today,' said Stu. 'Been walking a few years now, Rob. Gets me out of the house.'

'He's still a bit of a rookie,' said Geoff. 'I call him Stu the Foot.'

Stu sighed. 'Wore new walking shoes on my first long distance walk, Rob. Lost a toenail soon after. Not pretty.'

'A rookie rambl... long distance walking mistake.'

The bus drove away, leaving the three of us standing beside some houses in an estate.

'So the route I've created for us, which is most likely the way your Moonrakers would have gone,' said Geoff, 'will take us through an area where the army, in their wisdom, conduct night manoeuvres.'

'Night manoeuvres?'

'Yup. They spray a little live ammunition. Spray being the word with today's forecast. I'd say your chances of seeing the moon are about zero tonight. Hope your waterproofs are good.'

'Not sure they're good enough to keep bullets out.'

'Geoffrey,' said Stu, 'let's start with the map, shall we? We both know what you're like with directions.'

Geoff agreed this was a good idea and looked back at Stu.

'The map, Geoff?'

Geoff looked Stu in his eyes. 'I don't have the map. *You* have the map, Stu. I told you to pick it up, you daft sod.'

Stu and Geoff checked each of their pockets. And then each other's. Twice. But neither of them had the map. Not *the* map, with the coordinates and pubs and other important landmarks that would navigate us safely around the firing range. That was folded neatly on the corner of Geoff's kitchen table. Instead we had a pocket map that Stu had brought as backup, his glow-in-the-dark compass, and a small bottle of cherry brandy.

'I wanted to make the walk authentic,' said Stu, unscrewing the bottle. 'This is what the Moonrakers were all about, right? Don't drink it all now. We'll be out for a while with no map.'

He took a swig and passed it around.

That afternoon and evening, we sludged for ten miles along muddy tracks, following Stu's basic map and fluorescent compass. The rain didn't stop at any point but Stu's packed lunch of sandwiches and brandy kept our spirits pretty high. Like Geoff had warned, we had no chance of seeing the full moon tonight. Phoebe was stuck behind too many layers of cloud. I didn't mention my disappointment.

Inside the Lamb Inn, a pub Stu had just about guided us to, we got down to t-shirts and trousers, the rest of our soaked walking gear cooking above the open fire.

'So, this moon thing's all the result of a young lady?' asked Stu, coming back to our table with another three pints of beer.

'A young lady called Belle, yes.'

I shared an abridged version of the story.

'Ouch,' said Geoff. 'And how are you feeling now?'

'A lot better these last couple of months. I was back in Falmouth in November. I managed to let go of a lot.'

'Anyone new on the scene?' asked Stu.

'Someone magical called Phoebe.'

'And where did you meet Phoebe?'

Geoff and Stu offered plenty of life advice I still try to follow today. To not dwell much on the past. To enjoy the moment you're in because it's the only one you can truly experience. To look after yourself, because until you learn to do that you'll find it difficult to look after anyone else. And to always drink just one more beer before you leave the pub.

We tumbled out of the Lamb Inn a couple of hours later, dressed in our damp and foul-smelling socks and shoes. We were holding onto one another's shoulders.

'Where's the army?' I asked. 'I bet between the three of us we could take them on tonight. I'm powered by full moon.'

Geoff laughed. 'Oh yeah: that was a joke. I checked and there's no manoeuvres tonight. Gotcha.'

I'd spent the previous morning rubbernecking Stonehenge, which is your only option if you refuse to pay to walk around it. Close to Devizes, I wanted to see if I felt energy from this place of lunar worship. But it was heaving with people. And from what I could see, nobody was worshipping anything except themselves. The era of the selfie was beginning.

Thinking back to my November night on the beach, and how connected I'd felt to the pebbles, sea, air and sky, I noticed how distant these sightseers were from the place they were visiting. How detached they appeared behind their cameras and phones. Perhaps this is a madness of modern times.

There was no escaping the elements back on Salisbury Plain. Not one part of my body was dry by the time we reached a collection of buildings that looked to belong in the hills outside Rome rather than at the end of a lane in Wiltshire.

'What a place,' I said. 'Where are we?'

'Welcome to Roundway,' said Geoff, 'a former lunatic asylum. I'm no expert but I know local folk avoid this place. Lots of nasty things must have happened inside these walls. Especially on full moon nights like tonight, I hear.'

The word 'lunatic' dates back to the Late Latin *lunaticus*, or 'moon-struck'. It means crazy, irrational or insane. The belief was of course, as I'd seen throughout the year, that the moon— that distant rock, that reflector of light and energy—affects our emotions, and can send minds spiralling into madness. Or, if you believe in the Transylvania effect, the light of the moon can even transform people into wild creatures.

It was when I reread *Dracula* and found the character Renfield that 'lunatic' had come to life for me. Like many people with mental health issues back in the Victorian era, this young man with a taste for insects and blood was labelled and locked away in an asylum for his behaviour. He may well have experienced experimental treatments, like electroconvulsive shock therapy, now so controversial. Not as punishment but because nobody was sure how to deal with mental health at the time. It was easiest to blame the moon, that mysterious orb in the sky.

We didn't hang around long at the former Wiltshire County Lunatic Asylum. Although it became a hospital whose doors closed in 1995, my skin shivered at the thought of the anguish that must once have drifted along its corridors and through its wards. Roundway is now luxury apartments. We agreed we wouldn't want to live there.

Standing beside the Crammer in Devizes a little later, the moon nowhere to be seen but its influence everywhere, Stu handed me the brandy bottle for a final time. We'd walked thirteen miles—maybe fifteen if you include our three drunken orbits of Urchfont. There was enough brandy left for one sip each.

'This is it, I suppose,' I said, taking the bottle from Stu. 'The end of my year of moonwalks. Well, that was all fun. Thank you, chaps, for joining me on my last little adventure.'

I drank my share and handed the bottle to Geoff.

'Where are the fireworks? And the flashmob? At least Phoebe could have shown her face.' I knelt beside the Crammer and breathed deep.

'Not quite the ending you had in mind?' asked Geoff, taking off his black beanie and scratching his bald head.

I looked up to the clouds. 'Not really.'

Blue moon
Now I'm no longer alone
Without a dream in my heart
Without a love of my own

'Blue Moon',
Rodgers and Hart, 1934

Blue moon

A final surprise

I'd made my own rookie mistake.

In an error worthy of Geoff and Stu, I'd failed to note the final full moon dot on my almanac.

The moment I spotted it, soon after walking the Moonraker route from Orcheston to Devizes, I breathed my deepest and most relieved breath of the year. And realised something.

If I'd chosen to moonwalk any other year of my life, there would have been no International Year of Astronomy. No four hundred years since Harriot, Lower, Galileo and their Dutch trunkes. No forty years since Neil Armstrong's one small step.

The paranormal investigators might have missed my email. Dad might never have mentioned William Scoresby. I doubt I would have bumped into James in Walthamstow or Martin below the Tor in Glastonbury. And it seems highly unlikely there would have been a thirteenth full moon on the final day of the year.

I checked and double-checked and triple-checked my Gwydion's Moon Diary against other sources and it was true—there was another full moon on December 31st.

According to my Royal Observatory professor, Dr Pav, who'd become my most trusted source of moon facts, the Harriot to my Lower, this was a blue moon.

There are a couple of blue moon definitions, he told me. When a volcano erupts and the atmosphere fills with particles, the moon can appear blue. It sounded spectacular and I hoped to see it one day. But that wasn't this sort of blue moon. Today's was a second full moon in a calendar month, which occurs every two and a half years because of the difference between the 29.5-day synodic lunar month, full moon to full moon, and the months of the Gregorian calendar that most of us live by, which last 30 days, 31 days or whatever February fancies.

I felt elated that, after Phoebe's no-show beside the Crammer, I had another chance to see her. So I sat down at my parents' dining room table with a blank piece of paper and... had no idea what to do about this bonus moonwalk. Big, was my instinct. This walk needed to be bigger, bolder and more brilliant than all the others put together. So big that if Belle found out what I was doing, she'd see me for the real man I was and—

I stopped myself. No, this wasn't about Belle any longer. It was about me. Me, Phoebe and the people who had made this year unforgettable. I started to send some emails.

Two weeks later, on a crisp and icy winter's morning, I left my parents' house in Waltham Abbey on foot. The sun was distant and pale. It felt powerless on my skin.

'See you tomorrow morning,' I said, standing on the driveway.

'You not here for New Year celebrations tonight?' asked Mum. 'We've got Christine and Cliff over. Oh and Margaret and Omar.'

'Mick's popping in,' said Dad. 'Mick, Jan, maybe your aunt and uncle, too. Few beers? Watch the fireworks with us on TV?'

I gave my parents a kiss on their cheeks. 'It's blue moon. I'm going into London. I've got a lot of friends to meet, and places to visit. And did I tell you that I seem to have started a... sort of global moonwalking movement?'

'A what?' asked Dad.

A New York radio station had got in touch thanks to Louis, who'd started following me on Twitter in March. The host was keen to know more about Moonman and his moonwalks.

'There's a blue moon on New Year's Eve,' I said.

'Can we get involved with a moonwalk?' asked the host.

'Of course. Go out when the sun sets and watch the moon rise from the horizon opposite. As it—she, Phoebe—begins to arc high in the sky, start your walk.'

'And where should our moonwalk take us, Moonman, in case our listeners want to do their own?'

'That's the beauty of moonwalking,' I replied. 'It's a personal journey. If you have Phoebe there with you, whether she's showing her face or not, your path will reveal itself.'

Back in the Royal Observatory, almost a year after I'd started my journey, I visited the Planetarium and watched films about the cosmos. I now understood nearly every word.

In the café, I spoke to Roger, the astronomer I'd met in January.

'Sounds like the sort of adventure Cook and Columbus might have enjoyed,' he said. 'Where will you moonwalk tonight?'

'Thirteen moon sites around London to celebrate the thirteenth full moon of the year.'

I'd get the train to Syon House, Thomas Harriot's London residence. From there I'd go to visit the street where thousands of fans had celebrated Michael Jackson in June. Later I'd walk towards the London Eye, a giant Ferris wheel that I thought would make a great frame for a moon photo.

Throughout I'd keep close to the Thames because I liked how, as a tidal river, it was powered by the moon.

As I pulled the straps on my backpack, which contained as many moon books as I could squeeze in, I told Roger the London lunar landmark fact I'd read the night before; about the place that would become the last marker on my final moonwalk of the year. It was where I planned to leave my note to Belle. In doing so I'd accept that I'd never see her again.

'Haven't heard that London link before,' said Roger. 'If it's true, then we're a little more connected to the moon than we think.'

I reached the south west of London around lunchtime and headed straight for Syon House, where Harriot had lived and spent nights mapping the sky with his telescope.

With the moon and sun aligned and tugging at the Earth, the Thames had burst its banks. The bridge I'd planned to cross to get to Syon House was submerged in murky water. Even though I couldn't see Phoebe yet, I could feel her presence as I tiptoed through the flood she was causing.

Sadly, the house was closed. Instead of seeing Harriot's first moon sketch up close, I ambled around the grounds, crunching over grass, admiring frosted spider webs that hung like silver necklaces, watching red-breasted robins darting between trees, and puffing condensed breath. Respect nature and nature will respect you, I thought as I walked.

Back in the city, the streets were deserted. The Moon Under Water pub, where I drank a beer with Seb; a newly installed tidal clock at Trinity Buoy Wharf, where Phil joined me for lunch; the Millennium Dome, curving like a slice of lunar surface I circled alone. I enjoyed wandering in empty silence.

Close to Liverpool Street Station, where the Michael Jackson flashmob had danced into the night, I met my brother for coffee.

'Got a surprise for you, bro,' he said.

An hour later, we were on the forty-second floor of One Canary Wharf, in Natalie's office, waiting for the moon to rise over the Thames Estuary.

'It's not quite the sea,' said Natalie. 'But...'

'Belated birthday present, bro. When was that again?'

I was born on December 28th. In English common law, a lunar month was made up of four weeks, or 28 days. The word 'month' is related to the word 'moon'—months were defined as a lunar cycle. 'Monday' also comes from 'moon': it's the moon day that follows Sunday, named in honour of the sun. This year, my birthday fell on Monday 28th.

'Oh and this,' said David, handing me an envelope. 'Open it when you get to somewhere special. Somewhere moony.' He looked out of the window. 'Well would you look at that...'

David, Natalie and half the office, who'd stayed late to see this thing Natalie had tried to explain to them, turned to one another as the crimson moon rose from the horizon.

I smiled at my brother. 'Poxy moon?'

I reached the London Eye late in the evening. Phoebe was now high in her steep winter arc, while New Year partygoers were beginning to flood the embankment and bridges below. I stood among them for a moment, looking up.

Belle and I had met and fallen in love in London. We'd lived opposite each other in university halls here, and hung out together often around the city. I'd always thought of this city as our city. But I'd read something.

According to *The Cambro Briton*, a 19th-century publication I'd found online, ancient Britons called the moon llun, seemingly from the Latin, *luna*. While a dun was a fortified place, later a village, town or city. Instead of being the city of Rob and Belle, London was actually, I realised, the City of the Moon.

Later, in *Notes and Queries*, a journal started in 1849 and still running today, I read something even more exciting. That London had actually got its name from Lan Dian, or Llan Dian, a temple of Diana, the goddess of the moon, which had once stood at the site of St Paul's Cathedral. Story goes that Sir Christopher Wren discovered its remains while preparing to build.

It was now 11pm. Drunk people were everywhere around me, bumping and bashing and shouting and vomiting. Overhead, Phoebe was as precious as that first night I'd paid attention to her on the River Lee. Her light was cleansing, calming and hopeful. I began my walk to the Temple of Diana.

There, standing below the dome, I took out my notepad and opened it at the page with the words to Belle.

I read it once, then again. But I couldn't feel it any more. Too many of those emotions had passed. I started to edit myself, to try put into words how I felt about her now.

But nothing.

So I crossed it all out and wrote this in its place:

Phoebe
Thank you
For giving me light
When I felt so dark
And sharing your path
When I felt so lost
And bringing me friends
When I felt so alone
And for being here
When I needed you most
Rob x

I walked towards the cathedral. A step from its walls, ready to tear out and leave my note, a policewoman appeared.

'What are you doing, sir?' she asked. 'You realise you shouldn't be walking outside the cathedral at this time?'

'Do you know what day it is today?' I asked, tucking my notepad into my backpack.

'It's New Year's Eve. Are you drunk, sir?'

I asked her to look up.

'It's a blue moon,' I said. 'On the last day of the International Year of Astronomy. We're standing at the Temple of Diana, the goddess of the moon. Some call her Phoebe. She's looking beautiful tonight. Don't you think?'

The policewoman smiled. 'Sounds like you're a big fan of

Phoebe. Where's that come from?'

I put my backpack over my shoulders. 'It's a long story.'

The people around Big Ben and the Houses of Parliament were bashing about like sand hoppers.

While children waved sparklers in their gloved hands, their parents jostled for the best position to see the fireworks. I held back, taking a couple of blurry photos of Phoebe, who's a challenge to capture with a basic camera because of the amount of light she reflects.

I spotted a man with a telescope and DSLR set-up. It was Dr Pav, my moon expert from the Observatory. He'd emailed the evening before to say he'd be out here around this time.

'We finally meet,' he said. 'How's your final moonwalk?'

'Great. They've all been great. Any good shots of the moon?'

'A couple.'

Dr Pav showed me his evening's photos: such well-lit, detailed images of the lunar surface. Some so close up I felt I could leave my own footprint there. One shot stood out for the faint shadow that hovered over one of its edges. I asked the professor what I was looking at.

'There was a partial lunar eclipse, Rob,' he said. 'Which really does make tonight's full moon an incredibly rare event.'

The countdown to the end of my year began.

10...

I had no idea where to stand or what to do or what to think.

9...

Dr Pav was now surrounded by a group of his friends.

8...

So many people were pushing and squashing me.

7...

One hundred thousand revellers screaming.

6...

I breathed deep and focused on the moon.

5...

I pictured places I'd been, people I'd met.

4...

I thanked Belle for letting me go.

3...

Happy tears welled in my eyes.

2...

Phoebe was smiling wide.

1...

I smiled back, wider.

Clouds soon began to arrive at the celebrations.

Then, while the crowds cheered and fireworks rocketed to the sky and exploded into colour, and sleet like glitter sparkled through the air, I slid a signed document from the envelope my brother had given me earlier in the day. It was a certificate.

Turning my back to the mass of people, I read that I was now the custodian of an acre of land, my own 'estate', on the moon. A little piece of Phoebe was mine to look after forever.

And I could visit her any time I wished.

Reflecting

'Are you feeling her energy?' asked Debbie.

'Of course,' I said, holding my hands over a smoking joss stick. 'Day before, day of, day after. Did you see her last night?'

We were back in the cellar of White Witch on the first day of the new year. Debbie held her cup of tea in her fingerless gloves. Her sparkling eyes were reflecting a candle.

'We spent the evening with dear friends, Rob. We gathered in a tiny, thatched cottage, threw logs on a delicious fire and shared stories. Then we went out in the moonlight. It was so clear.'

I put my hand on Debbie's. 'Thank you for my tarot reading, Debbie. It was just what I needed back then. Gave me some hope at a difficult time. I'd like you to have something as a thanks.'

I placed my semilunar pen nib from Birmingham on the table.

Debbie picked it up and studied it in the warm candlelight. 'It's wondrous. I love it. It looks like the moon. Thank you, Rob.'

We walked to the top of the stairs. Looking across the market square, the snow was pristine except for my own footprints.

'May I ask you something, Rob?' said Debbie. 'I just wonder what you learned from your year living with the moon.'

'So much, Debbie. We'd need all day and a lot more tea.'

Debbie laughed. 'Top three. Please. Go on.'

'Ok. The first is definitely that you have to be good to yourself. Physically and emotionally. We're all vulnerable at times, and we need to learn to be loving to ourselves. I learned to be better and better as the year went on. Change the narrative I'd been telling myself.'

'Two?'

'That nature is just wow. Like really incredible. I spent more time in the wild last year than in... I don't know how long. And I loved it. A very wise man told me that we need to respect nature because then nature will respect us. I've definitely learned that being outside—regardless of whether it's the hottest day of the year or a snowstorm—is good for my mind.'

Debbie started to unlock the shop door. 'That's very much something I believe, too. It's so true. And your third?'

I opened the door. 'That the moon, Debbie—whether science can prove it or not—definitely affects us and our lives on Earth. I'm completely convinced about that. Like her phases, we're constantly changing. And like the tides she controls, our lives are always a movement of emotions. I've learned to accept those movements and changes. Just let them be. From now on, I'm going to try to put everything into what I'm doing and live in the moment.'

Debbie leant in and gave me a hug.

'So it's not all hocus-pocus and mumbo-jumbo then?'

'Not at all. I think it's something far more magical.'

After walking around Waltham Abbey's gardens, actually seeing and appreciating them and my local church for the first time, then feeding the ducks and geese and clearing snow from my mosaic, I strolled home for a warming a cup of tea.

Turning on my computer, I found almost one hundred messages, in email and Twitter, from friends and strangers across the country and around the world who'd enjoyed a moonwalk the night before, just as I'd encouraged in personal messages, tweets and on the radio show.

Moonraker John's photo of Phoebe above Wiltshire was perfect—a close-up of her freckles, lines and wrinkles. She looked like a well-aged Hollywood star, still shining bright.

Someone called Gordon had shared a photo from Thurso, in the north of Scotland. I could see great lines shooting from craters created by cataclysmic impacts. The *maria*—thought to be

seas by early astronomers, hence the marine-sounding name—
made Phoebe look weathered and wise. In fact Gordon had sent
me two photos. The second showed the blue moon eclipse, with
Phoebe's top-right edge just beginning to fade to shadow.

Todd, someone from Florida, had sent me a photo from
the night before New Year's Eve: 'The weather's looking pretty
soupy here, so I figured I'd get one while I can.' His moon was a
pleasing creamy fuzz. Overexposed, he told me, 'to capture the
stars, and get the lens flare.'

Bless Doe, a woman from Vermont, who'd sent me the story
of her New Year's Eve journey. It started:

*But tonight big snowflakes descend slowly to the ground. I leave
the thermometer and begin my moonwalk.*

I told my parents about the messages. They said how lovely
that a subject like the moon could bring people from around the
world together.

I spent the morning upstairs in my bedroom, arranging the
photos in an online gallery.

'Rob, your brother's here to say hello,' Mum shouted.

'Did you survive last night, mate? Come and tell me some
stories. Especially the one about your amazing brother who
bought you your best birthday present ever.'

'Coming!'

I opened my notepad, carefully tore out my thank-you note to the moon, slid it into the envelope with my deeds to a little patch of lunar surface, and squeezed it into the cupboard with my backpack, books, almanac, maps, telescope and torch.

A small collection of papers wrapped in a ribbon fell to the carpet. It was the poetry I'd written in the months after the break-up. I read a couple of pieces and smiled, realising how far I'd come—and what an adventure I'd just had. Closing the cupboard door, I wondered what other journeys I might have ahead of me. And how they might also influence my life.

After all, it's not what happens to you that makes you who you are, it's what you do in response.

Thank yous

To everyone I met on my journey, as well as those who offered such strong, patient support in the ten years that followed—as I developed the courage and craft to share my story—thank you. You were close when I waxed and even closer when I waned. Especially Susy M, Debbie, John S, Jamie J, David P, Maia, Darren B, Sam G, Becca S, Tim R, and Mum and Dad.

I must also thank a magical character without whose presence none of this could have happened. Phoebe, I thank you for helping me to see life in a smoother, happier, more loving light.